Ambroise Thomas

1811-1896

MIGNON

Opera in Three Acts
and Five Tableaux

By

AMBROISE THOMAS

Words by

MICHEL CARRÉ & JULES BARBIER

English Version by

DR. TH. BAKER

With an Essay on the
Story of the Opera by

H. E. KREHBIEL

G. SCHIRMER, Inc., NEW YORK

Printed in the U. S. A.

MIGNON

Characters of the Drama

MIGNON, a young girl stolen by Gypsies	Mezzo-soprano
FILINA, an actress	Soprano
FREDERICK, a young nobleman	Contralto
WILHELM MEISTER, a student	Tenor
LAERTES, an actor	Tenor
LOTHARIO, an Italian nobleman	Basso cantante
GIARNO, a Gypsy	Bass
ANTONIO, a servant	Bass

Townsfolk, Peasants, Gypsies, Actors and Actresses

The scene of Acts I and II is laid in Germany; of Act III in Italy

15470

MIGNON

Opéra-Comique in Three Acts and Five Tableaux

Words by

MM. MICHEL CARRÉ AND JULES BARBIER

Music by

AMBROISE THOMAS

First performed at the Théâtre Impérial de l'Opéra-Comique, Paris, November 17, 1866, with the following cast:

MIGNON,	Mezzo-Soprano,	MMES. GALLI-MARIÉ
PHILINE,	Soprano,	MARIE CABEL
WILHELM,	First Tenor,	MM. LÉON ACHARD
LOTHARIO,	First Singing Bass or Barytone,	BATAILLE
LAËRTE,	Second Tenor,	COUDERC
JARNO,	Second Bass,	BERNARD
FRÉDÉRIC,	Buffo Tenor,	VOISY
ANTONIO,	Speaking Part,	DAVOUST

The scene, in the first two acts, is laid in Germany; in the third act, in Italy.

Mignon.

A narration of the story of this opera may profitably precede a discussion of its origin and some of the vicissitudes through which it has passed. *Mignon,* the heroine of the tale, is a strange creature who in her infancy had been stolen from her home in Italy by a band of wandering Gypsies. By them she is brought up and compelled to earn her living by dancing. We meet with her first in the courtyard of a German inn, among whose guests are a troupe of actors who are on their way to the castle of a nobleman where their performances are to enliven a festival. In this company are *Filina,* an accomplished flirt, *Laertes,* a light-hearted servant of the tragic muse, and *Frederick,* a young gentleman dangling after the skirts of mistress *Filina,* with whom he is over head and ears in love. Another occupant of the inn is an aged harper, *Lothario,* whose words and acts indicate that a great sorrow has turned his mind awry. He is, indeed, an Italian nobleman who, crazed by the loss of his child and the death of her mother, is wandering about the earth as a minstrel seeking the daughter who, he is convinced, is still alive, though many years have passed since she was carried away by Gypsies. The actor-folk are making merry and have compelled *Lothario* to sit down to a cup of comfort with them, when a company of Romany mountebanks appear on the scene. Their dance is rewarded with applause and silver, whereupon the leader brings *Mignon* out of a cart, where she has been sleeping on the straw, and bids her perform the egg dance upon a carpet spread for her. The girl, angered by the laughter with which she is received, sullenly refuses, and the Gypsy leader is about to beat her when *Lothario* throws his arms about her in protection. The old man is thrust aside and the stick again raised over the head of *Mignon*, when *Wilhelm* enters the courtyard and rushes to defend her, threatening the life of her tormentor with a pistol. *Giarno* whines about his loss caused by the girl's disobedience, but *Filina* throws her purse to him and he takes himself off contented. *Wilhelm*, the newcomer, is a wealthy young gentleman, who, having finished his university studies, is seeing the world at his leisure. *Filina* has cast an auspicious and eager eye on him and now sends her friend *Laertes* to make his acquaintance, while she coyly retires within the inn, only to reappear when the men are in conversation and receive the homage of *Wilhelm*, already dazzled by her charms. The upshot of the matter is that *Wilhelm*, having nothing better to do, joins the theatrical company, accompanied by *Mignon*, whose release he had purchased from *Giarno*, and followed by the harper.

Arrived at the castle where the festivities are to take place, *Wilhelm* falls rapidly and deeply into the toils of *Filina*, to the unutterable grief of *Mignon*, who is now consumed with love for her deliverer. She notes the infatuation of *Wilhelm*, and in her jealous despair attempts to drown herself, but is restrained by the sound of *Lothario's* harp. To the minstrel she goes for help and comfort, but her imprecations against the castle inspire a wicked plan in the distraught mind of the old man. Actors and guests are in the midst of their rejoicings over the success of the theatrical entertainment when it is found that the castle is in flames;—the minstrel had fired it for *Mignon's* sake. The scene of confusion is increased by the discovery that *Mignon*, having been sent back for *Filina's* nosegays, is in the burning building. *Wilhelm* rushes in and brings out her unconscious form in his arms.

These are the incidents of the first two acts. In the third act we are transported to Italy. *Lothario*, himself unconscious of the fact, has brought *Mignon* to his ancestral palace in the land which had haunted her memory from childhood, but for which she has no name. It was to her only the land of golden oranges and burning roses, of blue skies and light-winged birds, of palaces peopled by marble statues—the land in which she wished to live, in which to die. *Wilhelm*, enlightened at last as to her love, has followed her, and *Filina* has followed him. He finds *Mignon,* and to *Lothario* confesses his purpose to purchase the palace for *Mignon,* who is now supremely happy in his love. *Filina's* coming almost gives her a death-blow, but *Lothario's* mental recovery, his recognition of the palace as his old home, deserted since he had set out on his wanderings in search of his child *Sperata,* and of *Mignon* as that child, bring all to a happy conclusion.

The incidents of this plot were drawn chiefly from episodes in Goethe's famous novel entitled "Wilhelm Meister's Lehrjahre," which has been done into admirable English by Carlyle. In this work the story of *Mignon* is only of subordinate interest, serving effectively to supply a romantic atmosphere to portions of the story and bringing pure and ennobling influences into scenes singularly deficient in them, but touching none of the real springs of the romance. This, in effect, is an exhaustive commentary on social and political life in Germany at the end of the eighteenth century. In constructing a romantic play out of the *Mignon* incidents, the librettists proceeded very much as they had done in the case of "Faust," which they had turned into an opera-book for Gounod a few years before;—they took out the incidents which were adaptable to the operatic manner, utilized the poet's pictures and sentiments, but poured all the borrowed material into the conventional operatic mould, thus making it serviceable to the conventional operatic manner. For this both "Faust" and "Mignon" have been severely faulted by German critics, who, indeed, would not have been true in allegiance to the masterpieces of their greatest poet had they not resented their despoliation by librettists bent only on providing an agreeable entertainment for the habitués of the lyric theatre. But the philosophy of "Faust" and the critical comment of "Wilhelm Meister" are not fit operatic material, whereas some of the incidents and people of the two works are cut out for opera. This fact is strikingly illustrated in the present case. No more perfect prototype for an operatic character of the *leggiera* class than *Filina* could be imagined; and each of her companions supplies an individual element of contrast. *Mignon* is the embodiment of pathos, the exemplar of the cantabile style; *Wilhelm* stands for youthful sentiment—fluctuating and variable because youthful; *Laertes* for that careless disposition which has excellent expression in the conventional idioms of the *buffo; Lothario* is lyricism incarnate. The *Mignon* of Goethe is a tragic type, and her death, inevitable under the circumstances, is one of the most moving incidents in Goethe's romance. Mr. Thomas's opera, having been written for the Opéra-Comique of Paris, had to have a happy ending (tragic operas being at the time reserved for the Grand Opéra), and the circumstance that in it *Mignon* marries *Wilhelm* instead of dying of a broken heart gave great offence to the Germans, whom the composer attempted to appease with a new *dénouement,* a "Version allemande" in which *Mignon* falls dead in the arms of her lover when she hears the voice of *Filina* repeating some of the flourishes from her polacca in the second act. The device proved futile, as it deserved. The *Mignon of* Carré and Barbier bears little more than an external resemblance to the *Mignon* of Goethe, and to kill her is wanton cruelty. The operatic change has altered her nature quite as much as *Gretchen's* was altered, but the two characters are not necessarily rendered less amiable by that fact. In the case of *Gretchen versus Marguerite*, a strict moralist might even plead that the French librettists lifted Goethe's maiden to a higher ethical plane than she occupies in the original drama. Goethe's *Gretchen*, despite her sweet innocency, is of coarser fibre than the *Marguerite* of the opera. The authors of the libretto made the character more gentle, even while emptying it of most of its poetic contents; and Gounod refined it still more by breathing ecstasy into all its music. Goethe's *Gretchen* eagerly returns *Faust's* kiss on her first meeting with him in the garden, and already at the second (presumably) offers to leave her window open and accepts the sleeping potion for her mother; it is the sudden, uncontrollable rush of passion to which Gounod's *Marguerite* succumbs. *Gretchen* remains in simple amaze that such a fine gentleman as *Faust* should find aught to admire in her, even after she has received and returned his first kiss, but *Marguerite* is exalted, transfigured by the new feelings surging within her.

"*Il m'aime! . . . quel trouble en mon . . . cœur!*
L'oiseau chante . . . le vent murmure! . . .
Toutes les voix de la nature
Semblent me répéter en chœur:
Il t'aime!"

But this is getting to be something like critical discussion, which is not the business of this prefatory essay, and a sidewise excursion besides. It may have its value, however, in directing attention to some of the changes which the opera has undergone. It was brought forward at the Paris Opéra-Comique on November 17, 1866. Its success was instantaneous. Within six months it had one hundred performances, and before the year was over this number was increased to one hundred and fifty. Twenty years later the performances still averaged half a hundred a year in Paris. Its vogue, which was very considerable, in London and New York, was due to Madame Christine Nilsson, who sang it in London on July 5th, 1870, and in New York on November 22d, 1871. The latter performance took place at the Academy of Music, under the management of Maurice Strakosch, the language being Italian and the parts being distributed as follows:

Mignon, ...	Mme. Christine Nilsson.
Filina, ...	Mlle. Léon Duval.
Frederico, ...	Mlle. Ronconi.
Guglielmo, ...	M. Capoul.
Lotario, ...	M. Jamet.
Laerte, ...	M. Lyall.
Giarno, ...	Sig. Coletti.
Zingarella, ...	Mlle. Bellon.

The circumstance that the part of *Frédéric*, quite inconsequential originally, and played by a man, is in this cast assigned to a contralto, is an evidence of the changes that had taken place between the first Parisian and the New York productions. In London the part had been given to Madame Trebelli, for whom the rondo-gavotte, "In veder l'amata stanza" ("Me voici dans son boudoir"), was arranged from the *entr'acte* music preceding the second act, and since then has always been sung by a contralto. For Madame Volpini, who sang the part of *Filina*, also in London, a florid air, "Alerta, Filina!" ("Alerte, alerte!") was introduced, but these changes were trifling compared with the transformations which the finale underwent. The form in which it is presented in this edition is the first rearrangement of the original finale, and that followed universally now, so far as I have been able to learn. *Lothario*, reclothed in his right mind, sees his daughter Sperata in *Mignon*, because of the latter's recognition of the girdle which she wore as a child, her mother's portrait, and her recollection of the childish prayer which she used nightly to utter. The scene then comes to a conclusion with an ensemble, *Mignon*, *Wilhelm* and *Lothario*, rejoicing in the mutual understanding finally established, the musical foundation of which is the melody of the romance of the first act based on a paraphrase of Goethe's "Kennst du das Land" ("Connais-tu le pays" in the first act). Originally this scene was much more extended. *Mignon* and *Wilhelm* are happy in each other's arms when the voice of *Filina* floats in at the window. *Mignon* pleads with *Wilhelm* to drive the siren away, and the two withdraw from the threatened presence. The scene changes. We are in the midst of a group of peasants who are making merry. *Filina* is on hand, accompanied by the faithful swain, *Frederick*. She orders breakfast, and while it is preparing sings a song in the measure of a *forlana*—an Italian dance in sextuple time, particularly beloved of the Venetian gondoliers, beginning

Paysanne ou signora,
Choisissez qui vous plaira!
Tant qu'au ciel le jour luira,
En ce monde on aimera!

The sentiment is that of the song which Shakespeare admitted to his comedy "Much Ado About Nothing":

"Sigh no more, ladies, sigh no more,
Men were deceivers ever,
One foot in sea, and one on shore,
To one thing constant never.
Then sigh not so,
But let them go,
And be you blithe and bonny,
Converting all your sounds of woe
Into hey, nonny, nonny!"

The melody of this *forlana*, changed in rhythm, is yet to be heard in the coda of the overture. *Mignon* is shocked by the heartlessness of *Filina*, but the latter advances to her and offers her hand in friendship and congratulation and graciously bestows herself upon *Frederick*. Enter a chorus of peasants, who acclaim *Lothario* as their old master, the Marquis of Cypriani; and then general rejoicing. The nature of the finale constructed to humor the *Pietät* of the Germans, has already been suggested. It is abrupt enough to please the most voracious devourer of penny dreadfuls. It proceeds like the original ending up to the moment when the voice of *Filina* is heard in a phrase of the polacca, "Je suis Titania." *Mignon* pleads that she be driven away lest she herself die of grief. *Wilhelm* exclaims: "Mignon! Filina"; *Lothario* echoes with, "My daughter! Filina!" but *Mignon*, staring fixedly at the actress, falls into her lover's arms and expires.

H. E. KREHBIEL.

NEW YORK, December 24th, 1900.

INDEX

Mignon.

Overture.

AMBROISE THOMAS.

f
cresc.
dim.
Andante. (♪=92.)
dim
pp
espressivo
sf
dim.
pp
dim.
pp espressivo
cresc.
dim.
poco ritenuto
pp
rit. e smorzando
ppp
mf
p
Ped.

Moderato, tempo di Polacca. (♩= 100.)

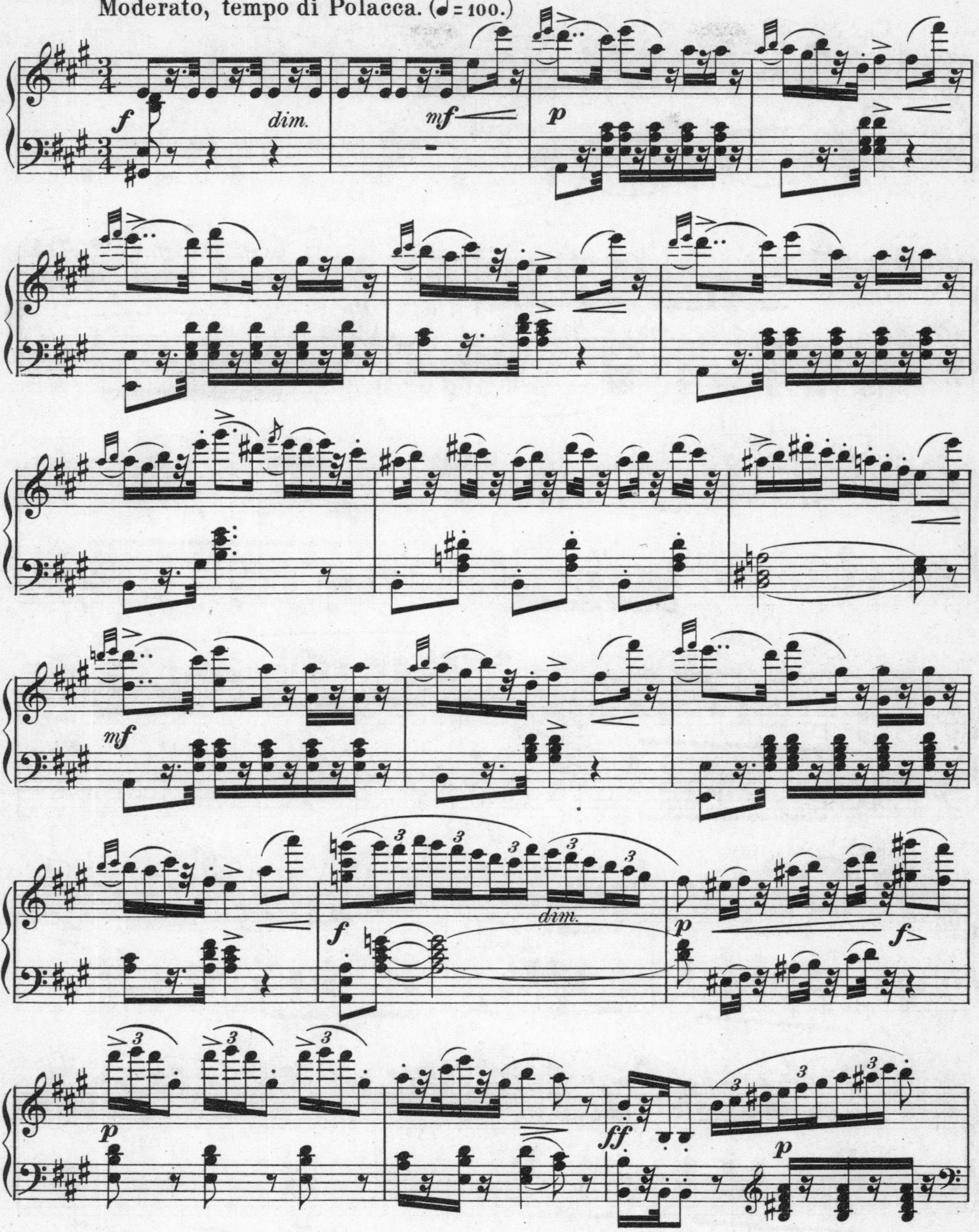

f *dim.* *mf* *p* *mf* *f* *dim.* *p* *f* *p* *ff* *p* *ff* *p* *ff* *p* *ff*

p
p
f
ff
dim.
p
p
f
mf

ff
dim.
p
p
dim.

pp
f
p
mf
tr
p
3
3
tr
pp
3
3
cresc.

ff
cresc.
ff
ff

p
mf
p
mf
sempre cresc.
ff

p *cresc.*

f

ff

Act I.

Nº 1. "Bons bourgeois et notables."

Introduction.

Scene, the courtyard of a German inn. L. H., the wing of a building which faces the audience; on the lower floor a door with glass window opens on a balcony, whence a flight of steps leads down to the courtyard. R. H., a low shed. Arbors, tables, etc.

Townfolk, peasants, etc., afterwards joined by Lothario; the townsfolk seat themselves at the tables, and drink; waiters bustle about, attending to their customers.

TENOR.
Chorus.
BASS.
Bons bour-geois et no-ta-bles, As-sis au-tour des ta-bles, Fu-
High or low-ly in sta-tion, Who hon-or our col-la-tion, We'll
mons, fu-mons tran-quil-le-ment, Et bu-vons en fu-mant.
smoke, we'll smoke like hon-est men, With a drink now and then.
Bons bour-geois et no-ta-bles, As-sis au-tour des ta-bles, Fu-
High or low-ly in sta-tion, Who hon-or our col-la-tion, We'll
mons, fu-mons tran-quil-le-ment, Et bu-vons en fu-mant. La
smoke, we'll smoke like hon-est men, With a drink now and then. Now

bière brune ou blan - che É - cu - me dans les pots.
foam - ing in the mea - sure Is beer, or brown or white;
ff
p
C'est au - jour - d'hui di - man - che, di - man - che,
This is a day for plea - sure, for plea - sure,
p
p
mf
mf
c'est le jour du re - pos,
'Tis a day for de - light,
mf
C'est au - jour - d'hui, au - jourd'hui di - man - che, C'est le
'Tis is a day, a day for plea - sure, 'Tis a

— le jour du re - pos, C'est le jour du re -
— day for our de - light, 'tis a day for de -

jour, le jour du re - pos, C'est le jour du re - pos, C'est le jour du re -
day for our de-light, day for our de - light, 'tis a day for de -

pos, le jour du re - pos. Que la biè - re brune ou blanche É -
light, day for our de - light. Now high foam - ing in the mea - sure Is

pos, le jour du re - pos. Que la biè - re brune ou blanche
light, day for our de - light. Now high foam - ing in the mea -

cu - me dans les pots! Mes a - mis, gaî - ment vi - dons les
beer, or brown or white; All our care we'll drown! Now drink it

É - cu - me dans les pots! A - mis, gaî - ment vi - dons les
sure Is beer, or brown or white; All care we'll drown! Now drink it

Andantino.
brocs!
down!
Andantino.
p
p
mf
p
Lothario.
(♪= 126.)
Lo.
Fu - gi - tif et trem - blant, je
Still from door un - to door all
dim.
Lo.
cresc.
vais, de porte en por - te, Où le ha-sard me gui - de, où l'o-
way - worn I am go - ing, Wher - ev - er Fate may guide me, or the

Lo.
p
ra - ge m'em-por-te; Des mi-sé-ra-bles Dieu prend soin.
storm-wind be blow-ing. For them who mourn, the Lord will care.
cresc.
f
dim.
p
El-le vit! El-le vit! et je cherche sa tra- - ce:
She's a-live! she's a-live! E'er do I seek her trac- - es:
cresc.
p
Je me repose un jour, un seul jour, et je pas-se! Je vais plus
Here will I rest a day, for a day swift-ly pass-es, Then fur-ther
dim.
p
loin, tou-jours plus loin, tou-jours plus
on, still on I fare, still on I

(1) See at the end of the score, in the Supplement, the *obbligato* ritournelle to the second strophe *(ad libitum)* of Lothario's song, as sung by M. Faure at London (page 340).

Lotharío sit down, and fill a glass for him.)

C'est aujourd'hui di - man - che, di - man - che, C'est le jour du re -
This is a day for plea - sure, for plea - sure, 'Tis a day for de -
pos,
light,
C'est au - jour - d'hui, au - jourd'hui di - man - che, C'est le jour, le jour du re -
This is a day, a day for plea - sure, 'Tis a day for our de -
Le jour du re - pos, C'est le jour du re - pos, le jour
day for our de - light, 'tis a day for de - light, day for
pos, C'est le jour du re - pos, C'est le jour du re - pos, le jour
light! day for our de - light, 'tis a day for de - light, day for
du re - pos. Que la biè - re brune ou blan - che É - cu - me dans les
our de - light! Now high foam - ing in the mea - sure Is beer, or brown or
du re - pos. Que la biè - re brune ou blan - che É - cu - me
our de - light! Now high foam - ing in the mea - sure Is beer, or

pots! Mes a - mis, gaî - ment vi - dons les brocs!
white! All our care we'll drown! Now drink it down!
dans les pots! A - mis, gaî - ment vi - dons les brocs!
brown or white! All care we'll drown! Now drink it down!
Andantino con moto. (♩ = 76.)
TENOR (Some peasants).
(Several of the party form a group at back, near the inn.
Enter Gypsies and Peasants of both sexes; Filina and
Laertes on the balcony; finally, Mignon.)
Place, a - mis, fai - tes
Room, compan - ions, make
pla - ce!
way there!
Place aux en-fants de Bo-
Room for the men of Bo-
hê - me, Aux tsi-ga-nes, aux zin-ga - ri!
he - mia, For the Gypsies let us make way!

March. Lo stesso movimento.
Chorus.
TENOR.
Voi-ci
BASS.
Of all
March. Lo stesso movimento.
tou-te la ban-de
their tribe the flow-er
a-vec Jar-no lui-mê-me,
is coming now with Giar-no,
Et son com-pè-re Za-fa-ri!
Zaf-fa-ri, too, his trust-y man!

(1) If it be necessary to abbreviate this march for a small stage, the next 14 measures may be cut, skipping to the sign ⊕ on page 22.

(1) In the following ballet with chorus there will be found two cuts *ad libitum;* but, if it be desired to omit the dance entirely, skip from here to the sign ⌖ on page 34.

F.
Mais ne vous moquez pas et so-yez in-dulgent;
But do not laugh at them, be in-dul-gent, I pray;
8
p
F.
3
A vous asseoir je vous in-vi-te.
To sit be-side me I in-vite you.
Gypsy Dance.
Allegretto sostenuto. (♩ = 100.)
p
legato
p
f

tr
tr
p
dim.
Chorus.
A group of old townspeople.
mf
Ces fil - les de Bo - hê -
The daughters of Bo - he -
8
f
mf
me Ont de forts jo - lis yeux, Et ma fem - me el - le mê -
mia, Their eyes are bright and gay, And my wife - can - not foot

Laertes.
Les fil-les de Bo-hê-me Ont
The daughters of Bo-he-mia Have
me Ne dan-se-rait pas mieux.
it More mer-ri-ly than they.
L.
d'as-sez jo-lis yeux, Et Phi-li-ne el-le-mê-me Ne dan-se-
eyes full bright and gay; Not Fi-li-na her-self e'en Could bet-ter
Filina (laughing.)
F.
O fil-les de Bo-hê-me, Fil-les au cœur jo-
O daughters of Bo-he-mia, With joy-ful hearts so
L.
rait pas mieux.
dance than they.
F.
yeux, Vous ai-mez, on vous ai-me, Et tout est pour le mieux.
blest, Ye love and are be-lov-ed, And all is for the best.

 (1) If desired, the next 16 measures may be omitted, skipping to the sign ⊕ on page 27.

SOP.
Fil - les d'É - gypte et de Bo - hê - me, Frap - pez le
Ye Gyp - sy and Bo - he - mian lass - es, Light - ly dance
TEN.
Fil - les d'É - gypte et de Bo - hê - me, Frap - pez le
Ye Gyp - sy and Bo - he - mian lass - es, Light - ly dance
BASS.
sol d'un pied jo - yeux!
on, in joy on - fare!
sol d'un pied jo - yeux!
on, in joy on - fare!
sol d'un pied jo - yeux!
on, in joy on - fare!
f
f
mf

cresc.
(♩. = 80.)
Allegro, tempo di Valzer.
Ped.
SOP.
TEN.
BASS.
Chorus.
Ah! chan - tez,
Sing, oh, sing!
gais en-
joy-ous
Ah! chan - tez,
Sing, oh, sing!
gais en-
joy-ous

(1) If desired, the next 32 measures may be omitted, skipping to the sign ⊕ on page 30.

Chorus.
Quel - - le dan-se fol-le!
How mad-ly they're danc-ing!
Quel - - le dan-se fol-le!
How mad-ly they're danc-ing!
f
Filina.
F.
La la, la la, la la, la la, la!
ff
Chorus.
Leur gai re-frain
Their gay re-frain
Nous met en
Charms us a-
Leur gai re-frain
Their gay re-frain
Nous met en
Charms us a-

p
train; Ah! Chan - tons! Ah! chantons! Et bu-
main! Let us sing! let us sing! let us
p
train; Ah! Chan - tons! Ah! chan-tons!
main! Let us sing! let us sing!
p.
ff
dim.
p
tr
vons! Ah! chantons!
drink! let us sing!
Et bu - vons! Ah! chan-tons!
let us drink! let us sing!
tr
f

f
Chan - tons! Bu-vons!
La danse fol-le
Sing! let us sing!
Mad-ly they're danc-ing,
Chan - tons! Bu-vons!
La dan-se fol-le
Sing! let us sing!
Mad-ly they're danc-ing,
ff
S'é-lance et vo-le, Leur jo-yeux re-frain Nous met tous en train!
Fly-ing, ad-vanc-ing! Joy-ful-ly sing-ing, Sway-ing and swing-ing!
S'é-lance et vo-le, Leur jo-yeux re-frain Nous met tous en train!
Fly-ing, ad-vanc-ing! Joy-ful-ly sing-ing, Sway-ing and swing-ing!

La dan - se fol - le S'é-lance et vo - le,
Mad - ly they're danc-ing, Fly - ing, ad - vanc-ing!
Ah!
Ah!
La dan - se fol - le S'é-lance et vo - le,
Mad - ly they're danc-ing, Fly - ing, ad - vanc-ing!
Ah!
Ah!
Chan - tons!
Now sing!
Chan - tons!
Now sing!

Allegro moderato. (♩=72)
Recit.
Giarno.
G.
Pour ga-gner main-te-nant tou - te votrein - dul - gen - ce, Et vous re-mer-ci -
To deserve to the full your gen-e-rous in - dul-gence, And ren-der fit-ting
er de vos dons gé-né - reux, Mi-gnon va vous prou-ver sa rare in-tel - li -
thanks for your lib - e - ral aid, Mi-gnon will now dis-play her rare and mar-v'lous
f
p
gen - - ce, En dan-sant de-vant vous le fa-meux pas des
tal - - ent By per-form-ing be-fore you her fa-mous dance on
f

G.
œufs.
eggs.
Chorus.
SOPRANO. ff
Vi - vat!
Hur - rah!
TENOR. ff
Vi - vat!
Hur - rah!
Rap-pro-chons-nous
Near-er let us
BASS. ff
p
ff
p.
La.
Laertes. p
Vo -
We
Rap-pro-chons-nous d'eux Pour voir la dan - se des œufs.
Near - er let us go, The fa - mous egg-dance to view!
d'eux
go,
Pour voir la dan - se des œufs.
The fa - mous egg-dance to view!
yons la dan - se des œufs.
too the egg - dance will view.
p

Giarno. (turning to Zaffari.)

G.

Toi! Za-fa-ri, pré-pa - re ton con-cer-to le plus sa-vant.
You, Zaf-fa-ri, be read - y To play the fin-est air you know;

(to the other Gypsies.)

Couvrez le sol d'un ta-pis ra - re.
Up-on the ground spread out the car - pet;

(approaching the cart and waking Mignon.)

Et toi, et toi, Mi-gnon, de-bout! en a-vant! en a-vant! — en a-vant!
And you, and you, Mi-gnon, get up! come a-long! come a-long! — come a-long!

(Zaffari preludes on his violin; an aged Gypsy spreads a carpet, on which a boy places some eggs. Mignon, hearing Giarno call, awakes and enters the circle formed by the chorus; in her hand she holds a bouquet of wild flowers.)

Filina.
(calling to Giarno.)
F.
Ho - là! Mon cher monsieur, vous plaît-il de nous
Hal - lo! my wor-thy man, be so kind as to
di - re Quel est — ce pauvre en - fant qui sem - ble vous mau -
tell us who is — this wretch-ed child, that fair - ly seems to
di - re De l'a-voir de la sor - te é-veil - lé sans fa - çon? Est-ce u - ne
hate you, That so rude - ly her slumber you have dared to an - noy? Is it a
Giarno.
F.
G.
fil - le? Est-ce un gar - çon? Ni l'un, ni l'au - tre, belle da -
maid - en? Is it a boy? Nor this, nor that one, mi - la -

G.
me,
dy;
Ni gar-çon,
nei-ther boy,
ni fil - le,
nor maid-en,
ni fem -
nor wo -
p
Filina.
F.
Qu'est-ce donc, a-lors?
But what is it, then?
(lifting the cloak that covers
Mignon. General laughter.)
G.
me!
man!
C'est Mi-gnon!
'Tis Mi-gnon!
pp
f
Mignon. (aside.)
M.
p
Ces yeux fi-xés sur moi, ce
Those eyes all fixed on me, So
f p
cresc.
M.
ri - re qui m'ou-tra - ge!
smil - ing, so in-sult - ing!
Re-trou-ve ta fier-
Re-gain thy for-mer
f

M.
G.
té, mon cœur,_ et ton cou-ra- ge!
pride, my heart,_ thy for-mer cour- age!
Giarno.
Al-lons,
Come a-
f
p
f
(stamping on the ground.)
sau-te, sau-te, Mi-gnon!
long, then! Dance now, Mignon!
Non, non, non, non, non! Je bra-ve ta me-
No, no, no, no, no! I dare de-fy your
na-ce, De t'o-bé-ir, à la fin, je suis las-se!
men-ace! 'Tis time at last! I no more will o-bey you!
Tu re-fu-
Not o-bey
ses! ho-là! vous au-tres, mon bâ-ton!
me? Hal-lo, my friends give me my stick!
(turning toward the Gypsies)
Non, non, non, non,
No, no, no, no,
(threatening her with the stick)
Dan-se, Mignon, ou mon bâ-
Dance now, Mignon, Or else a-

M.
non!
no!
non!
no!
G.
ton
non
Sau- ra te mettre à la rai-
You'll feel my stick your back up-
Chorus.
Dan- se,
Dance, then!
gare au bâ-
'Ware of the
G.
son!
on!
Dan- se,
Dance then,
al-
now
Elle a rai- son
Faith, she is right!
De di- re non!
Faith, she is right!
ton!
stick!
Dan- se, Mi- gnon!
Dance then Mi- gnon!
gare au bâ-
'Ware of the

Mignon.
M.
Non, non, non, non, non, non, non, non!
No, no, no, no, no, no, no, no!
G.
lons! Dan-se, Mi-gnon, Dan-se, Mi-gnon, Mé-
dance! Dance now, Mi-gnon, Now dance, Mi-gnon, you
Elle a rai-son! Elle a rai-son de
She's right, I own! she's right, I own, she's
ton! Dan-se, Mignon, Dan-se, Mi-gnon, Pe-
stick! Dance now Mignon! Now dance, Mi-gnon, you
(𝅗𝅥 = 76)
ff
G.
chant démon, Ou mon bâ-ton Sau-ra te mettre à la rai-son!
naugh-ty one! Or else a-non You'll feel my stick your back up-on!
di-re non! Elle a rai-son! Elle a rai-son de di-re non!
right, I own, she's right, I own, she's right, I own, she's right, I own!
tit démon, Ou son bâ-ton Sau-ra te mettre à la rai-son!
naugh-ty one! Or else a-non You'll feel his stick your back up-on!

G.
Dan - se, Mi - gnon, ou mon bâ - ton Sau-
Dance now, Mi - gnon, Or else a - non You'll
Elle a rai - son de di - re non!
she's right, I own! she's right, I own!
Dan - se, Mi - gnon, ou son bâ - ton
Dance now, Mi - gnon, Or else a - non
Sau-
You'll
G.
ra, sau - ra te mettre à la rai -
feel, you'll feel my stick your back up -
Elle a rai - son, elle a rai -
she's right, I own, she's right, I
sau - ra te mettre à la rai -
you'll feel his stick your back up -
ra, sau - ra te mettre à la rai -
feel, you'll feel his stick your back up -

(raising his stick.)
Lothario. (rising, and hastening to Mignon, whom he embraces).
Lo.
G.
son, Sau - ra te mettre à la rai-son!
on, you'll feel my stick your back up - on!
Re-
Poor
son, Elle a rai - son de di- -re non!
own, she's right, I own, she's right, I own!
son, Sau - ra te mettre à la rai-son!
on! You'll feel his stick your back up - on!
prends cou-ra-ge! Viens! pauvre en-fant, Con-tre sa ra-ge
child, take courage! I'll be your friend, you from his fu-ry
Je te dé-fends!
I will de-fend?
Giarno.
(angrily)
Au dia - ble, vil mi - sé - rable! au diable! au
Stand back there, wretch-ed old man! The Dev - il

G.
dia - ble! Dan - se, Mi - gnon, Mé - chant dé - mon,
take you! Now dance, Mi - gnon, you naugh - ty one,
Chorus.
Elle a rai - son, Elle a rai - son de di - re non!
She's right, I own, she's right, I own, she's right, I own,
Dan - se, Mi - gnon, Dan - se, Mi - gnon, Pe - tit dé - mon,
Dance now, Mi - gnon, Now dance Mi - gnon, you naugh - ty one,
G.
Dan - se, Mi - gnon, ou mon bâ - ton Sau-
Dance now, Mi - gnon, Or else a - non You'll
Elle a rai - son de di - re non,
she's right, I own, she's right, I own,
Dan - se, Mi - gnon, ou son bâ - ton
Dance now, Mi - gnon, Or else a - non
Sau-
You'll

G.
ra, sau - ra te mettre à la rai -
feel, you'll feel my stick your back up -
Elle a rai - son, Elle a rai -
she's right, I own, she's right, I
Sau - ra te mettre à la rai -
you'll feel his stick your back up -
ra, sau - ra te mettre à la rai -
feel, you'll feel his stick your back up -
G.
son, Sau - ra te mettre à la rai -
on, you'll feel my stick your back up -
son, Elle a rai - son de di - re
own! she's right, I own, she's right, I
son, Sau - ra te mettre à la rai -
on! you'll feel his stick your back up -
son,
on!
8

G.
son, Oui, pe - tit dé - mon, Oui, oui, mon bâ -
on! Yes! your back up - on, yes, your back up -
non! Oui, elle a rai - son, Oui, elle a rai -
own! yes! she's right, I own, yes, she's right, I
son, Oui, pe - tit dé - mon, Oui, oui, son bâ -
on! yes! your back up - on, yes, your back up -
sf
sf
G.
ton Sau - ra te mettre à la rai - son, Sau - ra te mettre à la rai -
on! You'll feel my stick your back up - on, you'll feel my stick your back up -
son, Elle a rai - son de di - re non, Elle a rai - son de di - re
own, she's right, I own, she's right, I own, she's right, I own, she's right, I
ton Sau - ra te mettre à la rai - son, Sau - ra te mettre à la rai -
on! You'll feel his stick your back up - on, you'll feel his stick your back up -

Filina.
Moderato sostenuto.
F.
Ah!
Ah!
Mignon.
M.
Ah!
Ah!
Wilhelm.
(rushing to help Mignon, and seizing Giarno's arm).
W.
Ho-là, co-quin! ar - rê - te, ou ton heure est ve-
Halloh, you rogue! Un - hand her, or your hour will have
Laertes.
La.
Ah!
Ah!
Loth.
Lo.
Ah!
Ah!
Giarno.
(raising the stick to strike Mignon).
G.
son!
on!
non!
own!
son!
on!
Moderato sostenuto.

(drawing a pistol, and threatening Giarno)
W.
nu - e! Si tu fais un seul pas, je te tu- -e!
sounded! If you dare take a step, I will kill you!
G.
Hein! plaît - il? C'est
Sir? you say? I
(in a whining tone)
G.
bon! je me tiens coi! Mais, je suis rui - né! Qui de vous me paie-
hear! I will be still! But, 'twill be my ru-in! Of you all, who will
Filina (throwing Giarno a purse).
F.
Tiens donc, prends, et tais-toi!... Que
Oh well! here! now be still! For-
G.
ra ma re - cet - te per - du- -e?
pay for the loss I shall suf- -fer?

Mignon. (dividing her bouquet between Wilhelm and Lothario)
F.
M.
tout soit par - don - né. À vous ces fleurs, a - mis,
give now, and for - get! Re - ceive these flowr's, oh friends,
M.
qui m'a - vez dé - fen - du - e!...
who were both my de - fend - ers.
Filina (aside).
Andante. (♪=120.)
F.
Quel est, je veux le sa-voir, Ce beau cou-reur d'a-ven-
I real-ly should like to know, who he is, this fine knight-
rit.
pp
F.
tu - re? Il nous ca-che sa fi-gu - re Et n'a pas l'air de nous
er - rant! He from us his face is hid - ing, Seems not to see us at
Laertes.
La.
Quel est-il?
Who he is?

Wilhelm.
F.
W.
voir.
all.
I -
Could -
p
dim.
La.
Ah, je le ju - re, Vous brû - lez de le sa -
Ah, well I see it! You're im - pa - tient now to
W.
ci, pou - vais - je pré - voir Cet - te bi - zar - re a - ven -
I ev - er have fore - seen such a sin - gu - lar ad -
La.
voir!
know!
cresc.
dim.
p
W.
tu - re! Mon cœur, pauvre cré - a - tu - re, M'a — seul dic - té mon de -
ven - ture! My heart, fol - lowing an im - pulse, On - ly my heart led me

Mignon (praying, aside).
W.
M.
voir. O Vier - ge, mon seul es - poir, Pro -
on. O Vir - gin, my hope thou art! Pro -
dim.
pp
M.
té - ge ta cré - a - tu - re, Je me
tect an in - no - cent maid - en Who be -
Laertes.
La.
Ce beau gar - çon à l'œil
This handsome youth, dark of
Filina.
F.
Quel est - il? je veux
Who is he? I wish
M.
cour - be sans mur - mu - re De -
fore thee, sor - row - lad - en, Now
Wilhelm.
p
W.
Cet - te a - ven - tu - re,
Such an ad - venture,
La.
noir, Quel est - il?
eye, Who is he?
dim.

F.
le sa - voir.
that I knew!
M.
vant ton di - vin pou - voir.
bends with a con - trite heart!
W.
Comment la pré - voir?
How could it be fore - seen?
Lothario (aside).
(Motionless, with vacant eyes; his hand strays o-ver the harp-strings.)
La.
Lo.
mf
Il faut le sa - voir. Sous le voi - le obs - cur du
I fain, fain would know. As her veil night spreads a -
mf
Lo.
soir, Et sous la ver - te ra - mu - re, Un homme à la lourde ar -
round, Where 'neath the boughs breezes mur - mur, A knight, clad in heav - y
sf
Lo.
mu - re Ar - rê - te son coursier noir, son coursier noir.
ar - mor, His cours - er halts at a bound, halts at a bound!
sf
dim.

Filina.
Ce coureur d'a-ven-tu - re Nous ca-che sa fi-gu-re;
He, the gallant knight-er - rant, His face from us is hid-ing;
Mignon.
Vier - ge sain-te, sois tou-
Ho - ly Vir-gin, ev - er -
Wilhelm.
Ah! com-ment pré - voir l'a - ven-tu - re!
How could I fore - see this ad-ven - ture!
Laer.
Ce coureur d'a - ven-tu -
Who is this bold knight-er -
Lothario.
Giarno.
Quel est-il, d'où vient-il? Ah! je veux le sa-
Ah, who and whence is he? Ah, that I fain would
Quel est-il? D'où vient-
Who is he? Whence is
Quel est-il? D'où vient-
Who is he? Whence is

F.
Quel— est - il? Ah! je veux le sa - voir!— Il n'a pas— l'air
Who— is— he? Ah, that I fain would know!— And he seems to
M.
jours mon— es - poir, mon seul es - poir;— sans mur - mu - re
more be— my hope, my on - ly hope!— Nev - er murm'ring,
W.
Pau - vre cré - a - tu - re, Je le ju - re!— Mon
This un - hap - py crea - ture! I de - clare it!— My
La.
re, Quel— est - il donc? ah! je le ju - re!— Vous— vou -
rant? Who— can he be? ah, I de - clare it,— that— you
Lo.
Sous le voi - le té - né - breux du soir— Il— est
As her veil the night spreadeth a - round,— He— is
G.
voir, Nous le saurons ce soir,— Oui,— je
know! This ev - 'ning we shall know!— Yes,— I
il? Quel— est - il?
he? Who— is he?
il? Quel— est - il? D'où— vient
he? Who— is he? Whence— is
cresc.
dim.
f
p

F.
de— nous voir,— Il n'a— pas l'air———— de— nous
see— us not,— It seems that us———— he— sees

M.
je— me cour - be de - vant—— ton di - vin pou -
now—— be - fore—— thee I bend—— with a con - trite

W.
cœur, oui, je— le ju - re! M'a dic - té mon de -
heart, yes, I— de - clare it! 'twas my heart led me

La.
lez———— dé - jà, vous vou - lez le sa -
fain———— would know, ah, how fain you would

Lo.
là!———— il est là!
there!———— he is there!

G.
veux———— le sa -
fain,———— fain would

Sor -
We'll

il? Sor -
he? We'll

F.
voir. Ah! quel est-
not. Ah! who is
M.
voir. O Vier - ge, Vier - ge, mon seul es -
heart! O ho - ly Vir - gin! my on - ly
W.
voir, Mon cœur, pau - vre cré - a - tu - re, Re-prends es -
on! My heart, un - hap - py crea - ture, has led me
La.
voir, Ce beau cou - reur d'a - ven - tu - re, Quel est - il
know! This hand - some, gallant knight - er - rant, Who can he
Lo.
Oui, sous la ver - te ra - mu - re, Oui, le voi -
'Neath boughs where breezes do mur - murs yes, he is
G.
voir, Nous le saurons ce
know! Ah, yes! I fain would
tons d'i -
go a -
tons d'i -
go a -
cresc.
dim.

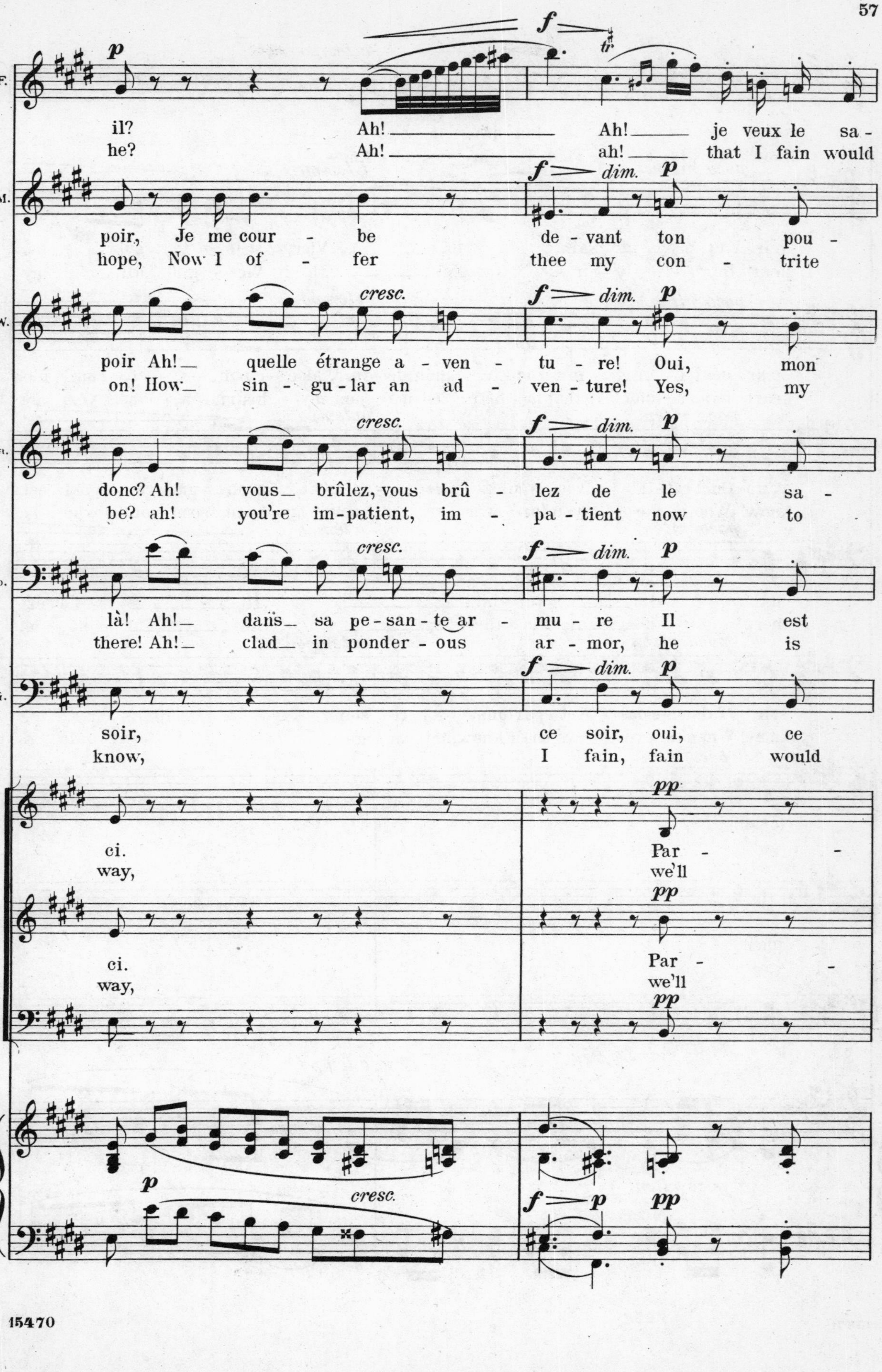

F.

il? Ah! Ah! je veux le sa-
he? Ah! ah! that I fain would

M.

poir, Je me cour - be de-vant ton pou-
hope, Now I of - fer thee my con - trite

W.

poir Ah! quelle étrange a - ven - tu - re! Oui, mon
on! How sin - gu-lar an ad - ven - ture! Yes, my

La.

donc? Ah! vous brûlez, vous brû - lez de le sa-
be? ah! you're im-patient, im - pa - tient now to

Lo.

là! Ah! dans sa pe-san-te ar - mu - re Il est
there! Ah! clad in ponder-ous ar - mor, he is

G.

soir, ce soir, oui, ce
know, I fain, fain would

ci. Par -
way, we'll

ci. Par -
way, we'll

p *cresc.* *f* *dim.* *p* *pp* *tr*

poco riten.
p
a tempo
F.
voir, Quel est-il? il fau-dra le sa-voir.
know! Who is he? That I fain would know.
poco riten.
a tempo
M.
voir. Vier - ge sain - te, Vierge sain-te, sois tou-
heart! Ho - ly Vir - gin! Ho-ly Vir-gin! all my
poco riten.
a tempo
W.
cœur seul i-ci m'a dic-té mon de-voir, Mon cœur i-ci, oui, mon
heart 'twas a-lone that has here led me on, my heart a-lone, yes, my
poco riten.
a tempo
La.
voir! Quel est-il? vous voulez le sa-voir, Ce beau gar-çon, quel est-
know! Who is he? you are fain to know! This hand-some youth, who is
poco riten.
a tempo
Lo.
là! Le voi-là! Il est
there! he is there! he is
poco riten.
a tempo
G.
soir. Taisons-nous et partons; à ce soir.
know! When'tis eve we shall know; let us go!
poco riten.
tons!
go!
tons!
go!
a tempo
cresc.
poco riten.

poco rit.
F.
Ah! je veux le sa-
Ah! I fain, fain would
poco rit.
M.
jours mon seul es- poir, mon es-
hope thou ev- er art! all my
poco rit.
W.
cœur m'a seul dic- té, m'a dic- té mon de-
heart a - lone, my heart, 'twas my heart led me
poco rit.
La.
il? ah! nous al- lons le sa-
he? ah! when 'tis eve we shall
poco rit.
Lo.
là! Ah! le voi- là! Il est là! le voi-
there! ah! he is there! he is there, he is
poco rit.
G.
Oui, nous re- vien- drons; à ce
yes, when we re- turn we shall
poco rit.
Oui, par- tons! à ce
yes, this eve we shall
poco rit.
Oui, par- tons! à ce
yes, this eve we shall
poco rit.
poco rit.
Ped.

a tempo

F. voir. know!

M. *a tempo* poir. hope!

W. *a tempo* voir. on!

La. *a tempo* voir. know!

Lo. *a tempo* là! there!

G. *a tempo* soir! know!

a tempo soir! know!

a tempo soir! know!

a tempo

(Exeunt townsfolk and others at back; Giarno retires

a tempo

to the shed with his comrade, followed by Mignon; Lothario withdraws slowly; Filina whispers to Laertes, indicating an interest in Wilhelm, thereafter entering her room, while Laertes descends the stairway to the courtyard.)

pp
dim.
rit.
Allegro moderato. Wilhelm (returning the salute).
W.
Mon - sieur...
Good sir!
Recit. Laertes (saluting).
p
L.
Mon-sieur...
Good sir!
souf-frez que l'on vous com-pli -
Al - low me, sir, to com-pli -
Allegro moderato.
men - te... Vous a-vez se-cou - ru cet-te gen-tille en-fant D'u-ne fa -
ment you! To the res-cue of this un-hap-py child you came, And in a

Wilhelm (smiling).
L.
W.
çon vrai-ment hé-ro-i-que et char-man-te! Bah! tout
way, in-deed, both he-ro-ic and charm-ing! An-y-
W.
au-tre en eut fait au-tant.
one would have done the same!
Laertes.
L.
Tel n'est pas l'a-vis de Phi-li-ne...
That is not th'i-dea of Fi-li-na:
(saluting again.)
L.
La dame du balcon a nom Phi-li-ne; moi, je me nom-me La-
The la-dy on the bal-co-ny's Fi-li-na; I bear the name of La-
(declaiming.)
L.
ër-te. O dé-sas-tre! O ru-i-ne! d'u-ne trou-pe co-
er-tes. Oh, dis-as-ter! Oh, what ru-in! Of a troupe of co-

(pompously.)
L.
mique aujour-d'hui sans emploi, Vous voyez en nous deux les débris mi-sé-ra-bles.
medians now out of employ, you behold in us two the un-hap-py re-mainder.
(in a natural tone.)
p
Phi-li-ne at-tend un sort meil-leur; Et moi, j'en-voie a-vec bon-
Fi-li-na hopes hap-pi-er days; with all my heart I'd send my
cresc.
heur No-tre mé-tier à tous les dia-bles!
art, ar-tists and all, straight to the dev-il!
(declaiming pompously.)
f
Mais un heu-reux ha-
But now a luck-y
allarg.
sard vous met sur mon che-min, Et je me fais hon-neur de tou-cher vo-tre
chance has put you in my way, And so I have the hon-or of tak-ing your

Allegro con moto.
(A waitress brings, on a tray, a bottle and two glasses.)
(they shake hands.)
Recit.
Wilhelm.
main.
hand.
Vous plaît-il a-vec moi vi-
May I call on your aid in
cresc.
Laertes.
der cet-te bou-teil-le?
emptying a bot-tle?
Sur ma foi! c'est par-ler d'or! Au
That you may! and with a will! Where
choc des ver-res pleins la gaî-té se ré-veil-le. Très vo-lon-tiers... Mon-
brimming glasses ring, there light hearts are a-wakened! With right good will Mon-
Wilhelm (to the waitress).
Un verre en-cor! Wil-helm Meis-ter, fils d'un bour-geois de
An-oth-er glass! Wil-helm Meister! My na-tive town's Vi-
sieur... Monsieur?...
sieur Monsieur

W.
Vien - ne, É - chap - pé, grâ - ce à Dieu! de -
en - na, but I fled, heav'n be praised! the
W.
puis un an à pei - ne, Des bancs de l'u - ni - ver - si -
u - ni - ver - s'ty bench - es a year, or some - what less, a -
W.
f
té, Heureux de mes vingt ans, fier de ma li - ber - té, Je veux cou - rir le
go; Rejoic - ing in my twen - ty years, and proud - ly free, A - round the world I'll
W.
mon - de!
wan - der! Laertes (declaiming.)
(emptying his glass.)
L.
f
Ô jeu - nes - se! Ô san - té!
Age of plea - sure! Youth and health! Allegro.
f
f

Nº 2. "Oui, je veux par le monde."

Aria.(1)

(1) This air is omitted at the Grand Opéra, Paris.

W.
dim.
sirs, je veux cou - rir gaî - ment!
sire: A - way with ev - 'ry care!
mf
Tout m'at - tire et m'en - chan - te,
All is gay and de - light - ful,
p
mf
Tout est nou - veau pour moi; Et je ris, et je
All things for me are new; And I laugh, and I
p
chan - te, Et ne suis que ma loi. Ô mai - son pa - ter -
car - ol, What I will, that I do! To the man - sion pa -
cresc.
nel - le, Je te fais mes a - dieux, Et j'ouvre en - fin mon
ter - nal I have bidden good - bye; My wings at last out -

dim.
W.
ai - le Comme un oi - seau jo - yeux! J'ou - vre en - fin mon
spread - ing, Gay as a bird I fly, Now my wings out-
ai - le Comme un oi - seau jo - yeux!
spread - ing, As gay as a bird I fly!
dim.
p
Oui, je veux par le mon - de Pro - me - ner li - bre - ment
Ay, a - round the world I'll wan - der, Free as bird in the air,
f
Mon humeur va - ga - bon - de, Au gré de mes dé - sirs
Nev - er long shall I pon - der What - e'er I de - sire;
Je veux cou - rir gaî - ment! Au gré de mes dé -
So a - way with all care! What - e'er my heart de -

cresc.
W.
sirs Je- veux cou-rir- gaî-ment,— Au gré de mes dé-
sires; A-way with ev-'ry care.— What-e'er my heart de-
cresc.
f
p
Je veux cou-rir
a-way with ev-'ry care!
W.
sirs cou-rir— gaîment!
sires; a-way— with care!
8
f
ff
p
dim.
Andante con moto. (♪ = 120)
Wilhelm.
dolce
W.
Si l'a-mour— sur ma rou-te Ce soir me tend la
And should love— chance to meet me This eve, joy-ous of
p
W.
main, Je m'ar-rê-te et j'é-cou-te Sans at-tendre à— de-
gaze, I shall tar-ry, I shall heark-en, Nor a-wait fu-ture

poco cresc.
W.
main! Mon cœur n'est point re-belle Au doux plai-sir d'ai-
days. My heart does not dis-dain The sweet de-lights of
mer, Et la voix d'u-ne bel-le Est prompte à me char-
love, And the voice of a fair one My soul will quick-ly
dim.
p
rit.
colla voce
un poco più lento
pp
mer! Mais la fem-me rê-vé-e Qu'on ap-pel-le tout
move! But the maid of my fan-cy, Whom I call on a-
sf
pp
rit.
bas, Je ne l'ai point trou-vé-e, Je ne la con-nais
side, I nev-er yet have found her, Nor know where she may
lento
pas. Ah! non! je ne la con-nais pas.
bide. Ah! no! Nor know where she may bide.

Allegro. Tempo I. ad lib.
W.
Est-el-le noble et bel-le?
Is she of beauty rarest?
Est-el-le
Of feature
brune ou blon-de? Peu m'im - por - te, vraiment! moi!
dark or fair-est? Not at all do I care! no!
cresc.
Variant.
accel.
dim. rall.
a tempo
Ah! Ah!
Ah! Ah!
Ah! Ah! Je veux, par le mon -
Ah! Ah! A-round the world I'll wan -
de, Pro - me-ner li - bre-ment mon humeur va - ga-bon -
der, Free as bird in the air, Nev - er long shall I pon -

W.
p
cresc.
- de, Au — gré — de mes — dé - sirs — je veux, — je veux cou - rir — gai-
- der What — e'er — my heart de - sires; — a - way, — a - way with ev - 'ry
f
dim.
ment! Je veux, — au gré de mes dé - sirs, je veux cou - rir — gai-
care! What-ev - er my heart may de - sire, a - way with ev - 'ry
ment! — Tout — m'attire et — men-
care! — All — is gay and de-
chan - te, Tout est — nou - veau — pour moi, —
light - ful, All things for me — are new, —
Et — je ris, — je ris et je
And — I laugh, — I laugh and I

W.
chante, Et ne suis que ma loi! Ah! Je ris, je ris et je
sing, What I will, that I do! Ah! I laugh, I laugh and I
chante, Et ne suis que ma loi! Oui, je veux par le mon - de Vo - ya -
sing, What I will, that I do! O'er the world will I wan - der, Free as
pp
p
ger li - bre - ment! Au gré de mes dé - sirs Je veux cou - rir gai -
bird in the air, Nev - er long shall I pon - der, So a - way with all
dim.
ment! Je veux tou - jours, oui, je veux, oui, je veux cou -
care! a - way, a - way, so a - way with all care, a -
smorz.
ppp
f
rir gaîment!
way with care!
ff

Laertes. Recit.
J'ai-me vo-tre gaî-té, j'ai-me vo-tre jeune
How I love your gay heart, your ar-dent youth's con-
(they drink)
â-me Plei-ne d'il-lu-si-ons, d'es-pé-rance et de flam-me!..
fes-sion, Of il-lu-sions yet full, full of hope and of pas-sion!
p
Wilhelm.
Vous me sem-blez heu-reux, Mal-gré les coups du
And you seem to be gay, de-spite the strokes of
sort?
fate.
Laertes.
In-fi-ni-ment, de-puis que je n'ai plus ma
I am, in-deed, since I from my wife have been
Vous fû-tes ma-ri-é!
Ah, then you have been mar-ried?
fem-me. Je le fus... et j'eus
part-ed! That I was; sor-ry

Moderato misurato.
f (singing)
L.
tort! A-mi, si tu veux m'en croi - re, Souviens-
state! My friend, should you long to mar - ry, Bear in
f
p
cresc.
toi de mon his-toi-re, Et ne va pas à ton tour Te prendre, te
mind my hap-less sto-ry, And nev-er cease to be-ware, Lest Cu-pid, lest
rit.
prendre aux pié - ges d'a-mour!
Cu - pid thy heart en-snare!
dim.
p segue
Recit.
Wilhelm.
W.
(indicating the balcony)
Vous cour-ti-sez pour-tant de fort près, j'i-ma-gi-ne, La da-me du balcon!
And yet you seem'd quite ar-dent-ly court-ing the la-dy Who sat be-side you there!
Allegro.
Laertes. (rather animatedly)
Qui? l'ai-ma-ble Phi-li-ne? Dieu m'en gar-de vrai-ment!
Who? the charm-ing Fi-li-na? Heav'n pre-serve me from her!

Wilhelm.
W.
Comment?
How so?
L.
Nous nous con-nais-sons trop pour nous ai-mer... Fol-le,
We know each oth-er far too well for love! Sil-ly,
L.
vai-ne comme pas u-ne, Plus per-fi - de que la for-tu-ne, Et plus chan-
vain as wo-man was nev-er, More in-con-stant than For-tune her fa-vor, And like the
L.
gean-te que la lu-ne, C'est grâce à son es-prit, et grâce à sa beau-
Moon, chang-ing for ev-er! 'Tis thanks to na-tive wit, and to her beau-ty
(Filina descends to the stage)
L.
té Le plus charmant dé-mon! Bu-vons à sa san-té!
rare, All hearts the fiend doth move! Her health! Sir, have a care!
mf
f
f

Nº 3. "Eh quoi! mon cher Laërte."

Trio.

Variant.
rit.
di - sent qu'il
give him the
W.
vè - re, Et vos beaux yeux, et vos beaux yeux di - sent qu'il
phras - es, Your love - ly eyes, your love - ly eyes give him the
Filina (to Wilhelm).
F.
Je vous sais gré du compli - ment!
I thank you for the kind re - ply!
ment!
lie!
(delightedly, aside)
Que de grâce et de
With an eye all - de -
f
p
char - mes! Quels re - gards pleins de feu! Les soupirs et les
fy - ing, Full of charm, full of grace, Here all weeping and

(1) The following solo for Filina may be omitted; in this case, skip from the second beat of this measure to the sign ϕ on page 82, at the beginning of Laertes' recitative "Permettez sans plus de façon", singing the first seven syllables to the tone *c*.

F.
mes,_ Si tou-te fem-me est com-me moi_ Co-quet-
to,_ If ev-'ry wo-man is like_to me,_ Co-quet-
-te, co-quet-te, lé-gère et sans foi, Hé-
tish, co-quet-tish and faith-less is she: Ah,
segue
las! que di-rons-nous des hom-mes? Que di-rons-nous-des hom-mes?
what shall we say of the men, too? what shall we say_of_men, too?
(indicating Laertes)
Combien j'en connais comme lui, Qui traî-nent chez nous leur en-
How man-y I know, such as he, Who drag to our door their en-
nui, Se vantant de ha-ïr les bel-les Qu'ils n'ont pas eu l'art de char-
nui, While they boast, how they hate the fair ones, Whom to charm they ne'er had the

dim. poco rit.
F.
mer,— Et qui nous traitent d'in-fi-dè-les Sans a-voir su se faire ai-
art,— And act as if we all were faith-less, Because they could not win our
a tempo
mer; Ils nous trai-tent d'in-fi-dè-les Sans a-voir su se faire ai-
heart, Act as if we all were faith-less, Be-cause they could not win our
dim.
mer; Ils nous trai-tent d'in-fi-dè-
heart, Act as if we all— were faith-
-les Pour n'a-voir su se faire ai-mer, Pour n'a-voir su se faire ai-
less, Be-cause they could not win our heart, be-cause they could not win our
Wilhelm. (laughing)
F.
W.
mer! Très bien dit! Vous voi-là ven-gé-e!
heart! True e-nough! Laertes. You are well a-venged!—
L.
Bra-vo! bra-vo! bra-
Well said! well said! well

Recit.
(presenting Wilhelm to Filina)
(presenting Filina
to Wilhelm)
vo! L'affaire est en-ga-gé-e. Per-met-tez, sans plus de fa-çon,
said! The fray is now be-ginning. Give me leave, with-out more a-do,
Qu'on vous pré-sen-te l'un à l'au-tre. Mon-
To one an-oth-er t'in-tro duce you. Mon-
sieur Wil-helm Mei-ster, un ai-ma-ble gar-
sieur Wil-helm Meis-ter, Ca-va-lier thro' and
çon, Qui vous of-fre son cœur en é-chan-ge du vô-tre. La Si-
thro', In ex-change for your heart will his own not re-fuse you! La Si-
gno-ra Phi-li-ne, Un an-ge en fal-ba-
gno-ra Fi-li-na, An an-gel whose wings will

L.
la, Qui vous trou - ve charmant et vou-drait vous le di - re.
grow; To her mind you are charming, and fain would she say it.
pp
(to Filina)
(to Wilhelm)
L.
Dé-co-chez à monsieur vo-tre plus doux sou ri - re! Offrez vo-tre bou-
Turning now to monsieur, your sweetest smile dis-play it! Now offer your bou-
Wilhelm.
L.
W.
quet à ma-da - me! Voi-là! Que de grâce et de-
quet to the la-dy! So-so! With an eye all - de-
f
p
Filina.
F.
p
Es - sayons de nos
Let us try all our
W.
char- - mes, Quels re - gards pleins de feu! Les soupirs et les
fy - ing, Full of charm, full of grace! Here all weeping and

F.
W.
L.
p
char-mes Pour nous ven-ger un peu, Es-say-ons de nos
charms, Now for re-venge, I say! Let us try all our
lar - mes Sont i-ci hors de jeu.
sigh - ing Would be quite out of place!
La belle est sous les ar - mes, Nous al-lons voir beau jeu.
She is now un-der arms, There will soon be a fray!
char-mes Pour nous ven-ger un peu, Me voi-là sous les
charms; Now for re-venge, I say! I am now un-der
Quels re- gards pleins de feu!
Full of charm, full of grace!
Oui, de-vant ses char - mes
And be-fore her charms
ar - mes; Le res - te n'est qu'un jeu! Es-say-ons de nos
arms, The rest is on - ly play! Let us try all our
Les sou - pirs, les soupirs
Here all weep-ing and sighs
Son cœur va prendre feu!
See his heart melt a-way!

F.
char - - mes; Me — voi - là sous — les
charms, — I — am now un - der

W.
Sont hors de
Are out of

L.
Nous al - lons voir beau jeu,
There will soon be a fray,

dim. *p*

F.
ar - - - - mes, Le res - te n'est qu'un
arms, — The rest is on ly

W. *p*
jeu. Quels re - gards pleins de feu! pleins de
place! Full of charm, full of grace! full of

L. *p*
Son cœur va pren - dre feu! pren - dre
See his heart melt a - way! melt a -

un poco animato *f*

F.
jeu. Ah! — Ah! — me voi -
play! on - ly

W.
feu! Ah! — quels re -
grace! Ah! — full of

L. *p*
feu! Son cœur va pren - dre, va pren - dre
way! His heart will melt, — will melt a -

f *p*

p cresc.

F. là! Ah!
play!

W. gards pleins de feu! Les sou-pirs, les lar- - -
charm, full of grace! All weep-ing and sigh- - -

L. feu! Elle est sous les ar- -
way! She's tak-en up arms,

F. Me voi-là sous les
I now am un-der

W. mes, Sont i-ci hors de
ing Would be here out of

L. mes, Nous al-lons voir beau jeu!
There will soon be a fray!

F. ar- - - - - - -
arms!

W. jeu, Les sou- -
place! Yes, all

L. Ah! la voi-là sous les ar-mes, Oui, nous al-lons voir beau
Ah, she now is un-der arms, And there soon will be a

F.
mes! Ah! Ah!
Ah! Ah!
W.
pirs, les sou - pirs et les
tears, yes, all tears and all
L.
jeu, Et de - vant tant de
fray! And be - fore all her
F.
Le res - te, le res - te pour moi n'est qu'un
The rest, all the rest, all the rest is on - ly
W.
lar - mes, oui, les sou - pirs et les lar - mes sont hors de
sigh - ing, yes, all weep - ing and all sigh - ing are out of
L.
char - mes, Oui, son cœur va pren - dre feu! Oui, va pren - dre
charms, See, his heart will melt a - way, yes, 'twill melt a -
cresc.
F.
jeu!
play!
W.
jeu!
place!
L.
feu!
way!

Allegro moderato.
Filina.
De mon a - mi, Mon - sieur, ex - cu - sez la fo -
Ex-cuse, I pray, Mon - sieur, all this gen - tle - man's
Wilhelm.
Recit.
Laertes.
Allegro moderato.
Piano.
(taking Laertes' arm.)
(simpering.)
F.
li - e; Vo 3 tre bras!
fol - ly! Give me your arm!
Com-
O -
Laertes
(to Wilhelm.)
L.
De-vons-nous vous re-trouver i - ci?
Shall we meet you lat - er here a-gain?
F.
ment! quand on m'a vue, est - ce qu'on fuit ain - si?
ho! Once hav-ing seen me, must one flee me, then?
L.
On fe - rait bien de
One would do well to
Allegro.

(aloud, curtseying.)
F.
La réponse est po-li-e! Im-per-ti-nent! Mon-sieur
You re-ply most po-lite-ly! How can you dare! Mon-sieur
sotto voce
L.
fuir! Co-quet-te! Mon-sieur
flee! You flirt, you! Mon-sieur
(Exeunt Filina and Laertes.)
a tempo
f
dim.
Wilhelm.
(gaily.)
f
W.
Voi-là, par-dieu! u-ne char-man-te fil-le, et La-
She is, in-deed, a charm-ing lit-tle wo-man! Tho' La-
f
f
W.
ër-te a beau di-re, Il n'est pas temps en-co-re de nous dire Un é-ter-nel a-
er-tes may say so, it is not time as yet for us to say fare-well for ev-er-
Mignon (coming from the shed.)
Wilhelm.
p
W.
M.
dieu. Il est seul! Ah! c'est toi?
more! He's a-lone! Ah, 'tis you?
p
dim.
mf

(These 2 measures will serve to transpose all that follows by a tone higher, in case Mignon's Romance is to be sung in *E♭*.)

No 4. "Demain, dis-tu?"
Recitative and Romance.

prefers to transpose the Romance into E♭, the tranposition must begin here by singing E instead
of D, and continuing to transpose this entire recitative,
both the vocal part and the accompaniment, a tone higher than it is written.)
M.
W.
C'é-tait mon pre-mier
He was my first
Le grand dia-ble, as-tu dit?
The great dev-il, did you say?
maî-tre.
master.
cresc.
Ce-lui qui t'a ven-due à cet hom-me, Ce-lui qui t'a vo-lée aux
Was it he who sold you to this fel-low, the man who stole you from your
tiens! Par-le, fais-moi con-naî-tre le pas-sé! je se-rai ton a-mi, ton ap-
home? Tell me, and let me know all of your past! I shall be your good friend, your sup-
Mignon (as if speaking to herself.)
p
pp
Hé-las! de mon en-
A-las! of all my
pui! Eh! bien? tu gar-des le si-len-ce?
port! How now? why are you still so si-lent.
fan-ce Un seul sou-ve-nir m'est res-té! J'er-rais au bord du
child-hood a sin-gle re-mem-brance is left! I wander'd by the

M.
lac par un beau soir_ d'é - té_ Des hommes in-con-nus, au vi-sa-ge fa-
lake one love-ly sum-mer eve: Then there were unknown men, men of wild, sav-age
M.
rou - che, Se dres-sent tout à coup dans l'om - bre au-tour de
fac - es, who sud-den-ly rose up in the shad - ows all a-
animandosi
cresc.
f
M.
moi!_ Un cri s'é-chap-pe de ma bouche! Je veux fuir!_ on m'en-lè - ve! on m'en-
round! There'scap'd my mouth a cry of ter-ror! I would fly! but they seize me, off they
Allegretto sostenuto. (♩. = 76.)
Wilhelm.
M.
W.
traî - ne!_
drag me!
Dis-moi, de quel-les pla-ges loin-
But tell me, of what far-dis-tant
f
mf
W.
tai-nes Ton âme a gardé sou-ve-nir_ Et si ma main brisait tes
coun-try a mem'ry yet lives in your mind? And were my hand to break thy
pp

W.
chaînes, Vers quels pa-ys ai-més tu voudrais re-ve-
fetters, T'ward what belov-ed land would your step be in-
rit.
Andantino. (♪= 120.)
W.
M.
Mignon.
dolce
nir!
clined?
Con-nais-tu le pa-ys où fleurit l'o-ran-
Dost thou know that fair land where the cit-rons
dim.
fp
p
M.
dim.
ger? Le pa-ys des fruits d'or et des roses vermeilles,
bloom? Where the or-an-ges' gold lights the leaf-y gloom?
M.
pp
Où la brise est plus douce et l'oi-seau plus lé-ger,
From azure skies ten-der breez-es gen-tly lave
pp
Ped. * Ped. * Ped. * Ped. *
M.
Où dans tou-te sai-son bu-ti-nent les a-beil-les,
Si-lent myr-tle-trees, and high the lau-rels wave.

sempre dolce
poco cresc.
M.
Où rayonne et sou - rit, comme un bienfait de Dieu, Un é - ternel prin-
Where so ra-diant - ly calm, like blessing from on high, Smiles an e - ter - nal
dim.
presto un poco
p
temps sous un ciel toujours bleu! Hé - las!
spring, ev - er blue is the sky! Ah me!
presto un poco
dim.
pp
Que ne puis - je te sui - vre Vers ce ri - vage heu - reux d'où le sort m'e - xi -
where - fore may I not wander Un - to that hap - py shore? Fain with thee I would
p
f
la! C'est là! c'est là que je voudrais vi - vre, Ai -
fare! 'Tis there! 'Tis there, in love ev - er fond - er, I
mf
f
p
mer, ai - mer et mou - rir! C'est là que je voudrais vi - vre, c'est
fain would live and die! 'Tis there, in love ev - er fond - er, I'd
mf
p

Allegretto.
M.
là! oui, c'est là!
live, I would die!
mf
Ped.
riten.
p
sf
dim. p
Andantino.
Mignon.
Con-nais-tu la mai-son où l'on m'attend là-bas? La
Hast thou e'er seen the house? In its pil-lar'd walls They
p
sal-le aux lambris d'or, où des hom-mes de mar-bre
stand wait-ing for me; how re-splen-dent the halls!
dim.

pp
M'ap-pel-lent dans la nuit en me ten-dant les
And forms of mar-ble stand and gaze on
pp
bras? Et la cour où l'on dan-se à
me: Hap-less maid-en, what sor-row o'er-
l'om-bre d'un grand ar-bre? Et le lac trans-pa-
clouds thy des-ti-ny? And the clear, shin-ing
poco cresc.
rent où glis-sent sur les eaux Mil-le bateaux lé-
lake, where-on there glides a-long Man-y a sway-ing
dim.
p
gers pareils à des oi-seaux! Hé-las!
boat with danc-ing and with song! Ah me!
dim.
pp

M.
— que ne puis-je te sui-vre Vers ce pa-ys loin-tain d'où le sort m'e-xi-
— where-fore may I not wan-der Un-to that happy shore? Fain with thee I would
la! C'est là, — c'est là que je voudrais vi - vre, Ai-
fare! 'Tis there, 'tis there, in love ev-er fond - er, I
mer, ai-mer et mou-rir! — C'est là que je voudrais vi - vre, c'est
fain would live — and die! — 'Tis there, in love ev-er fond - er, I'd
là, oui, c'est là!
live, I would die!
p
f
mf
dim.
pp
Ped.

Wilhelm (after the Romance in D).
W.
Ce pa - ys en - chan - té n'est - ce pas l'I - ta -
Is the name of this coun - try en - chant - ed not
Recit.
Wilhelm (after the Romance in E♭).
W.
Ce pa - ys en - chan - té n'est - ce pas l'I - ta -
Is the name of this coun - try en - chant - ed not
Recit.
Mignon.
M.
p
Je ne sais.
I know not!
Allegro. (Tempo of the Gypsy March).
(enter Giarno.)
W.
li - e? Cré - a - tu - re é - tran - ge!
I - ta - ly? Thou mys - te - rious be - ing!
Allegro.
p
mf
Giarno (with some animation).
G.
W.
Fort bien l'en - fant vous plaît, mon prince!...
Right well she pleases you, my prince!
Wilhelm (menacingly).
Sur ma vi - e n'a - jou - te pas un
'Pon my life! do not add anoth - er
sf
f

(threatening Giarno.)
W.
mot!...
word!
(sneeringly and roughly.)
mf
G.
Bon! je ne dis plus rien! Mais puis-que vo-tre
Good! I will say no more! But, as long as your
f
cœur s'in-té-resse à la bel-le, Rembour-sez-moi ce qu'el-le m'a coû-
heart is in-clin'd to the maid-en, pay me the sum that she has cost my-
Allegro marcato.
Wilhelm. (with
G.
W.
té, Et je re-nonce à tous mes droits sur el-le! Viens
self, and I'll re-nounce my rights in her for ev-er! Be't
f
p
resolution).
(looking at Mignon with interest.)
(exit with Giarno.)
donc! Je veux lui rendre au moins sa li-ber-té!
so! Her free-dom I at least will now re-store!

Mignon.
(to Lothario.)
pp
Li-bre! li-bre! est-ce vrai! Viens partager ma joi-e!
Freedom! freedom! Can it be! Join me in my rejoic-ing!
M.
fp
Toi qui m'as com-me lui Dé-fen-due au-jour-d'hui! Pour con-so-ler Mi-
You, like him, were my stay, My de-fend-er to-day! You, to con-sole Mi-
p
gnon c'est Dieu qui vous en-voi-e!
gnon, 'twas God who sent you hith-er!
Lothario.
p lento
Lo.
J'ai vou-lu te re-
'Twas my wish to be-
Hé-las! Pourquoi hâ-ter l'heu-re de nos a-
A-las! why has-ten the hour of bid-ding good-
voir a-vant de fuir ces lieux.
hold you, ere I went a-way.

M.
dieux? Où vas - tu?
bye? Whither now?
(raising his arms toward heaven.)
Lo.
Il le faut!
I must go!
Dé-jà les hi-ron-
See how the swallows
Allegro moderato.
del - les vo - lent vers le mi - di...
yon - der Fly to the south a - way!
Lo.
M.
Moi, je pars a-vec el - les.
With them I, too, will wan - der!
Mignon.
cresc.
Que ne puis-je à tra-vers l'es-
Had I pin-ions, I fain would
pa - ce fuir aus - si!...
fol - low, light as they!
Do-ne ton luth!
Give me your harp!
Lothario.
Le voi-ci!
Here it is!

Nº 5. "Légères hirondelles."

Duet of the Swallows.

Lothario.
Lo.
Le vieux luth s'é-veil - le sous ses jeu-nes doigts, Et
How the chords a - wa - ken! How they sing, re - joice! Nor
Mignon.
M.
Fu-yez! Lé-
A-way! Ye
dim.
sem-ble, ô mer-veil - le! Ré-pondre à sa voix.
am I mis - ta - ken: They an-swer her voice!
sf
p
gè-res hi-ron-del - les, Oi-seaux bé-nis de Dieu, Ou-
swallows lightly fly - ing, And pois-ing high in air, Your
pp
Lé-gè-res hi-ron-
Ye swallows lightly
vrez, ouvrez vos ai - les, En-vo-lez-vous! A-dieu! En-vo-lez-
air - y pinions ply - ing Now wing a-way, a-far! Now wing a-
del - les,
fly - ing,
En-vo-lez-vous!
Now wing a-way,

cresc.
p
M.
vous! — Ouvrez vos ai - les, Lé-gè-res hi-ron-del-les, Ou -
way, — your pinions ply - ing, Ye swallows light-ly fly-ing, Air -
cresc.
p
Lo.
— Ouvrez vos ai - les, En-vo-lez-vous, lé-gè-res hi-ron-del-les,
— your pinions ply - ing, Now wing a-way, ye swallows light-ly fly-ing,
cresc.
p
cresc.
f
dim. legg.
- vrez vos ai - les, En-vo-lez-vous,
- i - ly ply - ing, Now wing a-way,
f
dim.
legg.
Ou - vrez vos ai - les, En - vo - lez-
Air - i - ly ply - ing, Now wing a -
f
dim.
p
p
en-vo-lez-vous, a - dieu! Fu-yez vers la lu-
now wing away, a - far! I fain your flight would
p
vous, a-dieu! a - dieu!
way, away, a - far!
sf
pp

M.
Lo.
miè - re, Fu-yez vi - te là - bas, vers l'ho-ri - zon ver-meil! Heu - reu-se la pre-
fol - low, Far a - way, ev - er on, till rosier skies are won! Ah, joy - ful is the
Fu-yez!
Away!
cresc.
miè - re Qui re - ver - ra, de - main, le pa - ys du so - leil. En - vo - lez -
swallow, Who first shall see, to - mor - row, the land of the sun! Now wing a -
A - dieu!
Fare-well!
mf
dim.
vous, a - dieu! Lé - gè - res hi - ron -
way! Fare - well! Ye swallows lightly
p
Lé - gè - res hi - ron - del - les, Oi - seaux bé - nis de
Ye swallows light - ly fly - ing, And pois - ing high in
dim.
del - les, a -
fly - ing, fare -
Dieu! Ou - vrez, ouvrez vos ai - les, En - vo - lez - vous, a -
air, Your air - y pinions ply - ing, Now wing a - way, a -

cresc.
p
M.
dieu! En-vo-lez-vous, ouvrez vos ai-les, Légè-res
well! Now wing a-way, your pinions ply-ing, Ye swallows
Lo.
dieu! En-vo-lez-vous, ouvrez vos ai-les, en-vo-lez-vous, Légè-res
far! Now wing away, your pinions ply-ing, now wing away, Ye swallows
f
dim.
hi-ron-del-les, Ou-vrez vos ai-
light-ly fly-ing, Air-i-ly ply-
legg.
les, en-vo-lez-vous, en-vo-lez-vous, a-
ing, Now fly a-way, now fly a-way, a-
les, En-vo-lez-vous, a-dieu! a-
ing, Now fly a-way, a-far, a-
dolce
sf
dieu! Légè-res hi-ron-
far! Ye swal-lows light-ly
dieu! Légè-res hi-ron-del-
far! Ye swal-lows light-ly fly-

M.
del - les, Oi-seaux bé-nis de Dieu, Ou-
fly - ing, And pois-ing high in air, Your
Lo.
les, Oi-seaux bé-nis de Dieu, A - dieu! Ou-
ing, And pois-ing high in air, Fare - well! Your
dim.
p
rit.
a tempo
vrez, ou-vrez vos ai - les, En-vo-lez-vous, a - dieu!
air-y pin-ions ply - ing, Now wing a-way, a - far!
vrez, ou-vrez vos ai - les, En-vo-lez-vous, a - dieu!
air-y pin-ions ply - ing, Now wing a-way, a - far!
pp
Variant.
ad lib.
ah!
a - dieu!
fare-well!

(bursts of laughter from Filina, outside.)
Recit.
(dragging away Lothario.)
M.
En-cor cet - te fem-me! Ah! viens! viens, te
A-gain comes that la-dy! ah, come! come, I
Allegro moderato, movimento del Duo.
(exeunt Mignon and Lothario.)
dis - je!
tell you!
p
f
Filina. (enters laughing.)
Recit.
F.
Ah! ah! ah! ah! ah! Ah! ah! ah! ah! ah! Com-
Ah! ah! ah! ah! ah! Ah! ah! ah! ah! ah! What
Frederick. (entering with Filina.)
Fr.
ment? c'est vous!
now? 'Tis you?
Frederick.
(dusting himself with his riding-whip.)
Oui, oui, ri - ez! je suis un
Yes, laugh a - way! A fool was

(mockingly)
F.
Ne vou-lez-vous pas que je
Shall I fall a weep-ing to
Fr.
sot De cre-ver mon cheval pour vous re-voir plus tôt.
I, that I fin-ish'd my horse, the soon-er to see you!
F.
pleu - re?
please you?
Vous pouvez re - par -
You can take your-self
Fr.
Ah! Vous me fai - tes re-pen-tir d'ê-tre ve - nu.
Ah! you will cause me to re-pent that I have come!
p
f
F.
tir, Vous nous re - vien-drez tout à l'heu - re.
off! You will come a - gain, in a hur - ry!
Wilhelm (to Giarno).
W.
(Enter Wilhelm and Giarno.)
Mar-ché con -
The bar-gain's
f
F.
Qu'entends-je là? vous a - vez ra - che - té Mi -
What do I hear? You have ran-som'd the child, Mi -
W.
clu! Mignon est li - bre.
clos'd! Mignon's at free-dom!

F.
gnon? Ce beau trait n'a rien qui m'é-ton-ne de vo-tre
gnon? This good deed in no way sur-pris-es, com-ing from
Giarno (going away.)
G.
L'af-faire est bon-ne.
Not a bad bar-gain!
part!
you!
Frederick.
Fr.
Hein? d'où sort ce-lui-là?
Ha! Who's here all at once?
(presenting Frederick.)
Monsieur Mei-
Mon-sieur
mf
p
(to Wilhelm.)
ster, je vous pré-sen-te Le jeu-ne Fré-dé-ric, un pe-tit é-co-
Meister, let me pre-sent you young Fred-e-rick, my friend; Tho' a student, he's
lier, Qui mal-gré moi s'est fait mon che-va-lier; Un fou d'humeur plai-
here A-gainst my will, to play the ca-va-lier; A gay, sil-ly young

F.
san-te, qui tour à tour M'ac-ca-ble de sa hai-ne! ou bien de son a-
fel-low, who day by day Is ei-ther sure he hates me, or loves me in a
(presenting Wilhelm to Frederick.)
F.
mour! Mon-sieur Wilhelm Mei-ster, un hom-me que peut-
way. Mon-sieur Wil-helm Mei-ster! A man whom in the
mf
p
F.
ê-tre Vous ai-me-rez un jour, Pour-vu qu'il
fu-ture you may in-cline to love, on-ly pro-
3
(coquettishly.)
F.
dai-gne vous pro-met-tre De ne pas me fai-re la
vid-ed he will prom-ise that he will not pay me his
F.
cour. Ah! vraiment!
court. Ah! in-deed!
Wilhelm (aside to Filina.)
W.
Je ne veux rien pro-met-tre, qu'à vous-mê-me.
I care to make no promise but to you.
Frederick (aside.)
Fr.
La co-
The co-
p

F.
W.
Fr.
L.
La.
(aside)
Il m'ai-me!
He loves me!
Ah! voi-ci La-
Ah! here is La-
(aside.)
Elle est charman-te!
She's real-ly charming!
Laertes. (outside.)
quette!
quette!
Phi-li - ne! Phi - li - ne!
Fi - li - na! Fi - li - na!
ër - te.
er - tes.
(entering.)
Tiens! bon-jour Fré-dé-ric! vous i -
Ah! well met, Fred-e-rick! Are you
(laughing.)
Il a cre-vé pour nous son che - val!
'Twas for our sake he fin-ish'd his horse!
(turning to Frederick.)
ci?
here?
Pau-vre bê - te!
Oh, poor crea - ture!

(Frederick seems annoyed.)
(quickly.)
(to Filina and Wilhelm, declaiming *largamente.*)
La.
Je par-le du dé-funt. A-mis, soy-ons en fê - te! Nous tri-omphons du sort ja-
I'm speaking of the dead! My friends, let us be mer - ry! Triumph is ours o'er jealous
F.
Pour moi?
For me?
W.
Wilhelm.
Li-
Do
(to Filina, in a natural tone.)
La.
loux! Les au-tres vont ve-nir, cet-te lettre est pour vous.
Fate! The others all will come, and this note is for you.
Laertes and Frederick.
Li-
Do
Filina (reading.)
W. F.
sez!
read it!
"Ma tou-te bel-le! Pour fê-ter digne-ment et
"Fair-est of la-dies! Be-ing anxious to hon-or
La.
sez!
read it!
(Read this letter *a tempo* instead of singing.)
Fr.
sez!
read it!
m.d.

F.
de fa-çon nouvel - le Le pas-sa - ge du prince Ul - ric de Tif-fembourg, Je vous at-
in a fitting manner the ar-ri - val of Ul - rich, Prince of Tieffen-burg, I look for
tends, ain - si que La-erte et les au - tres, En mon castel, a - vant la fin du
you, La - er - tes, and all the oth - ers, here at my castle, ere the day shall
jour. Je compte bien, mon cœur, que vous se - rez des nôtres; vous de - vi - nez mon tendre es-
close. I dare assume, dear heart, that you will be a - mong us; you will di - vine my ten - der
poir Et le doux bonheur que je rê - ve! Mon car - ros - se viendra vous chercher; à ce
hope and the dream of joy that inspires me! I shall send you my carriage in time: Do not
pp
poco cresc.
soir! et, si vous ré - sis - tez, cruelle, on vous en - lè - ve. Ba - ron de Rosem-
fail! for if you should re - sist, oh cru - el fair! they'll seize you! Baron von Rosen-
segue

(laughing.)
F.
berg."
berg."
Hein? comment? le Ba-ron est vo-tre oncle? C'est char-
What? in-deed? Is the Baron your un-cle? That is
Frederick.
Fr.
Mon on-cle!
My un-cle!
Hé-las! oui!
Yes, worse luck!
(turning to Wilhelm.)
mant!
good!
A-vec em-pres-se-ment!
I shall, glad-ly e-nough!
Vous ac-cep-tez son of-fre?
Shall you ac-cept his of-fer?
misurato
Vous, monsieur, s'il vous plaît prendre part à la fê-te,
You, dear sir, if you care to take part in the fest-al,
Libre à vous de ve-nir; sui-vez vo-tre dé-sir. Vous jouerez par-mi
you are wel-come to come; let in-clin-a-tion lead. You will play, if you

F.
nous le rô-le de po-è-te; Si vous ve-nez d'ail-leurs, vous me fe-rez plai-
join us, the rôle_ of a po-et; and should you real-ly come, I shall be glad, in-
F.
sir. Quant à vous, si vous o-sez me sui-vre, Sans pi-tié je vous
deed. As for you, if you should dare come af-ter, I shall show you no
Recit.
Frederick.
Fr.
Phi-li-ne!
Fi-li-na!
F.
li-vre Au courroux de monsieur votre on-cle! Bon-soir!
grace, but de-li-ver you to your un-cle! Good-bye!
(ascends to her room, and closes door)
Fr.
Mais...
But_
Frederick (in a passion).
Fr.
cresc.
Maudit Ba-ron! maudit mes-sa-ge! Maudi-te co-quet-te! Au re-voir, La-
Confounded note! confounded Ba-ron! Confounded co-quette! We shall meet, La-

Wilhelm.
W.
Plaît - il?
What now?
Laertes.
La.
So-yez plus
Be not so
(turning to Wilhelm).
(dons his hat, and exit precipitately).
Fr.
er - te! Vous, Mon-sieur!
er - tes! Sir, your servant!
sa-ge Que ce jeune é-tour-neau qui s'attache à nos pas! Sui-vez vo-tre che-min!
fool-ish as that sil-ly young man who still follows our steps! Pro-ceed up-on your way!
rit.
(presses Wilhelm's hand, then reënters thetavern).
Par-tez, et bon vo-ya - ge!
De-part! may luck at-tend you!
f a tempo
Wilhelm (after a short pause).
(resolutely)
Vous sui-vre en ce châ - teau, Phi-li - ne? Pour-quoi
Go with you to this cas-tle, Fi-li-na? And why

Nº 6. "Me voici! Tu m'as rachetée."

Trio and Finale.

W.
vil - le où le sort t'a je - té - e, D'hon - nê - tes
town where by fate you have drift - ed, some hon - est
sf
M.
Mignon.
Pour-quoi
But why
W.
gens chez qui tu se - ras bien trai - té - e.
folk, by whom you will be kind - ly treat - ed.
M.
W.
Wilhelm (smiling).
3
me sé - pa - rer de toi! Je ne puis t'em - me - ner a - vec
may I not stay with you? My poor girl, I can nev - er take
f
p
W.
moi, pau - vre fil - le! Et m'im - po - ser les
you on my wan - d'rings! I can - not un - der -

Mignon.
M.
W.
Ne peux-tu m'ha-bil-
Can you not dress me
soins d'un pè-re de fa-mil-le.
take the du-ties of a pa-rent.
ler comme un jeu-ne gar-çon, Et me lais-ser por-
up in the garb of a boy? For then I could be
cresc.
Wilhelm.
ter ta li-vré-e? A quoi
wear-ing your liv-er-y. To what
cresc.
dim.
Mignon.
bon? En-vers qui me dé-li-vre, Je vou-lais m'ac-quit-
end? To you, who are my sav-ior, I would fain show my
segue
ter! J'é-tais prête à te sui-vre Pour ne plus te quit-ter!
thanks. To fol-low you I'm read-y, I would leave you no more!

Wilhelm.
M.
W.
Des mains de ce sau-va-ge Li-bre pour un peu d'or,
From cru-el hands de-liv-er'd, Freed for a lit-tle gold,
Mignon.
dolce
W.
M.
Quel nou-vel es-cla-va-ge Veux-tu su-bir en-cor? En-
To what new kind of bond-age Would you so fain be sold? To
dim.
pp
M.
vers qui me dé-li-vre, Je vou-lais m'ac-quit-ter! J'é-
you, who are my sav-ior, I would fain show my thanks! To
Wilhelm.
W.
p
Quel nou-vel es-cla-
To what new kind of
M.
tais prête à te sui-vre Pour ne plus te quit-ter!
fol-low you I'm read-y, I would leave you no more!
W.
va-ge Veux-tu su-bir en-cor?
bond-age Would you so fain be sold?
dim.

(imploringly)
(sadly)
M.
Ne plus te quit-ter!
I'd leave you no more!
C'est bien!
'Tis well!
W.
cresc.
Non!
No!
Non!
no!
pp
puis-que ta main, sans pi-tié, me re-pous-se,
Since with a pit- -i-less hand you re-pulse me,
(indicating Lothario)
Lothario (hastening to Mignon and embracing her).
M.
Lo.
Je pars a-vec lui!
With him I shall go!
Viens! la li-bre
Come! Gai-ly a
segue
Lo.
dim.
mf
vie est dou- -ce! À
free life pass- -es! In
dim.

Lo.
l'om - - bre des grands bois,
shade of might - y woods,
pp
6
sous le ciel é - toi -
'neath a star - - - light - ed
lé
sky,
p
Nous
A
trou - ve-rons un lit de fou - gère et de
rest - ing-place we'll find on the grass and the
mous - - se,
moss - - - es,
Et
Thou

cresc.
Lo.
tu par-ta-ge-ras le pain de l'e-xi-
shalt par-take the ex-ile's bread in peace-ful
Lo.
lé! Viens! tu par-ta-ge-ras le pain
joy! Come! par-take the ex-ile's bread
Lo.
de l'e-xi-
in peace and
(about to lead Mignon away)
Wilhelm (stopping him).
Lo.
W.
lé!
joy!
Non! pauvre en-
No, my poor
cresc.
W.
fant! pour toi l'a-ve-nir m'é-pou-van-te!
child, I fear for the fu-ture be-fore you!

cresc.
W.
Reste a - vec moi, si tu le veux! Le sort _ en est je - té! Je me rends à tes
Re-main with me, if you de - sire! Our fate _ will have it so: I will do as you
f
p
M.
Mignon.
En-
To
W.
(kindly)
dim.
vœux! _ L'a - mi qui te dé - li - vre Ne doit plus te quit - ter,
will! ___ The friend who was your sav - ior should for - sake you no more!
pp
M.
vers qui me dé - li - vre Je pour - rai _ m'ac-quitter,
you, who are my sav - ior, I would fain _ show my thanks,
W.
L'a - mi qui te _ dé - li - vre
The friend who was _ your sav - ior _
Lothario.
L.
Dieu bon! Dieu bon! lais - se - moi vi - vre, Es - pé - rer! _
Oh Lord! Oh Lord! For life I pray Thee! Let me hope! _

M.
W.
L.
cresc.
Je suis prête a te sui-vre, Je ne veux plus te-quit-ter! Je pour-
I am read-y to fol-low, I would leave you no more! Might I
Ne doit plus te quit-ter, ne plus te-quit-ter! Al-
should for-sake you no more, for-sake you no more! In-
Je veux, je veux vi-vre, Es-pé-rer et chanter! Dieu
For life I pray thee, let me hope, let me sing! Oh
rai m'acquitter! Ah! ja-mais! Non, je ne
on-ly show my thanks! Nev-er-more! No I will
lons, il faut, il faut cé-der! Non,
deed, I must, I can but yield! No,
bon! Dieu bon! ah! lais-se-moi, lais-se-moi
Lord! Oh Lord! ah! let me hope! For life I
veux plus te quit-ter! te quit-ter!
leave you nev-er-more, nev-er-more!
je ne dois plus te quit-ter!
I will for-sake you no more!
vi-vre, lais-se-moi vivre et chan-ter!
pray thee, let me hope, ah, hope and sing!

Wilhelm.

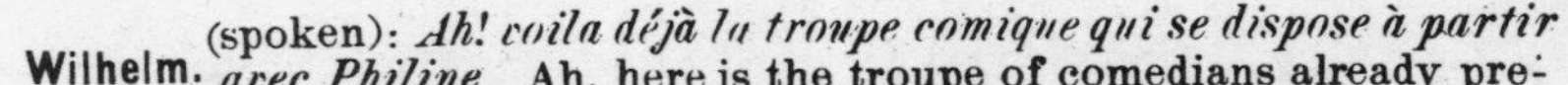
(spoken): *Ah! voila déjà la troupe comique qui se dispose à partir avec Philine.* Ah, here is the troupe of comedians already preparing to accompany Filina.

Allegro moderato. (♩. = 112.)

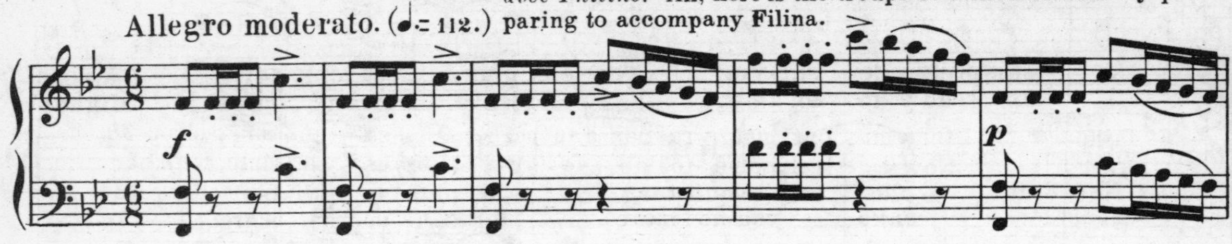

(Enter Comedians, dressed for a journey, and carrying bags, parcels, etc.)

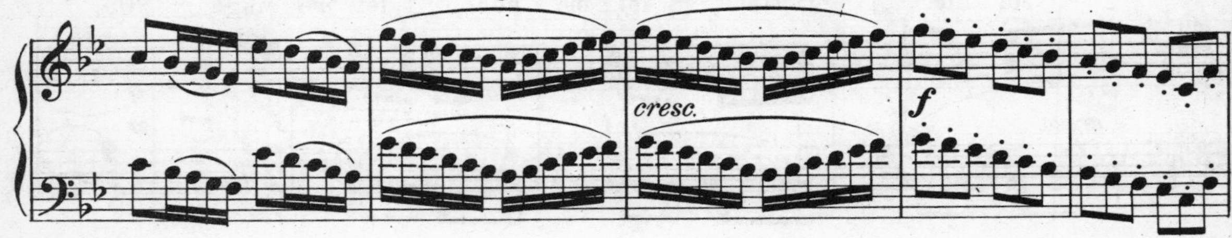

faim! Ou - bli - ons nos re - pas d'au - berge, Et sa - lu - ons, cha - peau le -
o'er! Now a wel - come to ap - pe - tite! Let us sa - lute, with hat in
f
vé, Ce vieux_cas - tel où l'on hé - ber - - ge Les his - tri -
hand, This old_chá - teau, where they in - vite All the co -
p
ff
ous sur le pa - vé! Al - lons, a - mis, pli - ons ba -
me - dians' need - y band! A - way, my friends, let us be
Plions ba - ga - - - -
Let us be go - - - -

ga - ge!
go - ing!
Partons, la chance nous sou - rit en - fin! allons!
Forwards! Dame Fortune is smil - ing once more! Away!
ge! Allons, a - mis!
ing! A-way, ye friends!
al-lons, par-tons!
let us a - way!
Gypsies.
Giarno with the Basses.
Heureu - se chan - ce!
Oh how surpris - ing!
Jour de bomban - ce!
Day of re - joic - ing!
Heureu - se chan - ce!
Oh how sur-pris - ing!
A - dieu la
Farewell to

Comedians.
En route, a-
A-way,_ ye
soif, a-dieu la faim!
thirst! Hunger, fare-well!
En route, a-
A-way,_ ye
mis, pli-ons ba-ga- - -ge, La chance nous sou-rit en-
friends, let us be go- - -ing! Dame Fortune is smil-ing once
mis, pli-ez ba-ga- - -ge, La chance vous sou-rit en-
friends, let all be go- - -ing! Dame Fortune is smil-ing once

fin! Ou - bli - ons nos re - pas d'au - berge, Et sa - lu -
more! Now a wel-come to ap - pe - tite! Let us sa -
fin! Ou - bli - ez vos re - pas d'au -
more! Now a wel-come to ap - pe -
ons, cha - peau le - vé, Ce vieux_ cas - tel où l'on hé -
lute, with hat in hand, This old_ châ - teau, where they in -
ber - ge, Sa - lu - ez ce vieux_ cas - tel où l'on hé -
tite! And sa - lute this old_ châ - teau, where they in -
f

(1) A cut may be made by skipping from the sign ⊕ to the same sign on page 143, repeating the chord in the 2nd measure.

li- -ne Que le ba-ron des-ti- -ne
Ba- -ron has pro-vid-ed, I'll wa- -ger,
C'est, je ga-ge à Phi-li- -ne Que le ba-ron des-
For Fi-li-na the Ba- -ron has pro-vid-ed, I'll
Ces la-quais é-légants, Ces la-quais é-lé-
These va-lets all so fine, These va-lets all so
ti- -ne Ces la-quais é-lé-gants,
wa- -ger, These va-lets all so fine,
8
gants Et ces che-vaux fringants, Ces la-quais é-lé-
fine And these hors-es di-vine, These va-lets all so
Ces che-vaux, ces la-quais é-lé-
These va-lets, these va-lets all so
cresc.

Actresses & Women of town and country.
gants?
fine!
La
Dame
gants?
fine!
La
Dame
gants?
fine!
La
Dame
Actors & Townsfolk.
En route,_ a - mis, pli - ons ba - ga - - ge, La
A - way,_ ye friends, let us be go - - ing, Dame
En route,_ a - mis, pli - ez ba - ga - - ge, La
A - way,_ ye friends, let all be go - - ing, Dame
En route,_ a - mis, pli - ons ba - ga - - ge, La
A - way,_ ye friends, let us be go - - ing, Dame
En route,_ a - mis, pli - ez ba - ga - - ge, La
A - way,_ ye friends, let all be go - - ing, Dame
Gypsies & Peasants.
En route,_ a - mis, pli - ez ba - ga - - ge, La
A - way,_ ye friends, let all be go - - ing, Dame
dim.

chan-ce nous sou-rit en - fin! Ou-bli - ons nos re-pas d'au-
For-tune is smil-ing once more! Now a wel-come to ap- -pe-
chan-ce vous sou-rit en - fin! Ou-bli - ez vos re-pas d'au-
For-tune is smil-ing once more! Now a wel-come to ap- -pe-
chan-ce nous sou-rit en - fin! Ou-bli - ons nos re-pas d'au-
For-tune is smil-ing once more! Now a wel-come to ap- -pe-
chan-ce vous sou-rit en - fin! Ou-bli - ez vos re-pas d'au-
For-tune is smil-ing once more! Now a wel-come to ap- -pe-
chan-ce nous sou-rit en - fin! Ou-bli - ons nos re-pas d'au-
For-tune is smil-ing once more! Now a wel-come to ap- -pe-
chan-ce vous sou-rit en - fin! Ou-bli - ez vos re-pas d'au-
For-tune is smil-ing once more! Now a wel-come to ap- -pe-
chan-ce nous sou-rit en - fin! Ou-bli - ons nos re-pas d'au-
For-tune is smil-ing once more! Now a wel-come to ap- -pe-
chan-ce vous sou-rit en - fin! Ou-bli - ez vos re-pas d'au-
For-tune is smil-ing once more! Now a wel-come to ap- -pe-
chan-ce vous sou-rit en - fin! Ou - bli-
For-tune is smil-ing once more! Now a
p

berge, Et sa-lu-ons, cha-peau le-vé, Ce vieux_cas-
tite! Let us sa-lute, with hat in hand, This old__châ-
berge, Et sa-lu-ez, cha-peau le-vé, Ce vieux_cas-
tite! Let all sa-lute, with hat in hand, This old__châ-
berge, Et sa-lu-ons, cha-peau le-vé, Ce vieux_cas-
tite! Let us sa-lute, with hat in hand, This old__châ-
berge, Et sa-lu-ez, cha-peau le-vé, Ce vieux_cas
tite! Let all sa-lute, with hat in hand, This old__châ-
berge, Et sa-lu-ons, cha-peau le-vé, Ce vieux_cas-
tite! Let us sa-lute, with hat in hand, This old__châ-
berge, Et sa-lu-ez, cha-peau le-vé, Ce vieux_cas-
tite! Let all sa-lute, with hat in hand, This old__châ-
berge, Et sa-lu-ons, cha-peau le-vé, Ce vieux_cas-
tite! Let us sa-lute, with hat in hand, This old__châ-
berge, Et sa-lu-ez, cha-peau le-vé, Ce vieux_cas
tite! Let all sa-lute, with hat in hand, This old__châ-
ez vos re-pas d'au-ber-ge, Sa-lu-ez ce vieux_cas-
wel-come to ap-pe-tite! And sa-lute this old__châ-

tel, où l'on hé - ber - ge Les his - tri - ons sur le pa -
teau, where they in - vite All the co - me - dians'need - y
tel, où l'on hé - ber - ge Les his - tri - ons sur le pa -
teau, where they in - vite All the co - me - dians'need - y
tel, où l'on hé - ber - ge Les his - tri - ons sur le pa -
teau, where they in - vite All the co - me - dians'need - y
tel, où l'on hé - ber - - ge Les his - tri - ons sur le pa -
teau, where they in - vite All the co - me - dians'need - y
tel, où l'on hé - ber - - ge Les his - tri - ons sur le pa -
teau, where they in - vite All the co - me - dians'need - y
tel, où l'on hé - ber - - ge Les his - tri - ons sur le pa -
teau, where they in - vite All the co - me - dians'need - y
tel, où l'on hé - ber - ge Les his - tri - ons sur le pa -
teau, where they in - vite All the co - me - dians'need - y
sf
ff

vé! Al-lons, a-mis, Pli-ons ba-ga-ge,
band! A-way, ye friends, Let us be go-ing!
vé! Al-lons, a-mis, Pli-ez ba-ga-ge,
band! A-way, ye friends, Let all be go-ing!
vé! Pli-ons ba-ga-ge, Al-lons, a-
band! Let us be go-ing! A-way, ye
vé! Pli-ez ba-ga-ge, Al-lons, a-
band! Let all be go-ing! A-way, ye
vé! Al-lons, a-mis, Pli-ons ba-ga-ge,
band! A-way, ye friends, Let us be go-ing!
vé! Al-lons, a-mis, Pli-ez ba-ga-ge,
band! A-way, ye friends, Let all be go-ing!
vé! Pli-ons ba-ga-ge, Al-lons, a-
band! Let us be go-ing! A-way, ye
vé! Pli-ez ba-ga-ge, Al-lons, a-
band! Let all be go-ing! A-way, ye
vé! Al-lons, a-mis, Pli-ez ba-ga-ge,
band! A-way, ye friends, Let all be go-ing!
vé! Pli-ez ba-ga-ge, Al-lons, a-
band! Let all be go-ing! A-way, ye

Par-tons, la chan-ce nous sou-rit en-fin! Al-lons!
For-wards! Dame For-tune is smil-ing once more! A-way!
Par-tez, la chan-ce vous sou-rit en-fin! Al-lons!
For-wards! Dame For-tune is smil-ing once more! A-way!
mis, Par-tons, la chan-ce nous sou-rit en-fin! Al-lons!
friends! For-wards! Dame For-tune is smil-ing once more! A-way!
mis, Par-tez, la chan-ce vous sou-rit en-fin! Al-lons!
friends! For-wards! Dame For-tune is smil-ing once more! A-way!
Par-tons, la chan-ce nous sou-rit en-fin! Al-lons!
For-wards! Dame For-tune is smil-ing once more! A-way!
Par-tez, la chan-ce vous sou-rit en-fin! Al-lons!
For-wards! Dame For-tune is smil-ing once more! A-way!
mis, Par-tons, la chan-ce nous sou-rit en-fin! Al-lons!
friends! For-wards! Dame For-tune is smil-ing once more! A-way!
mis, Par-tez, la chan-ce vous sou-rit en-fin! Al-lons!
friends! For-wards! Dame For-tune is smil-ing once more! A-way!
Par-tez, la chan-ce vous sou-rit en-fin! Par-tez!
For-wards! Dame For-tune is smil-ing once more! A-way!
mis, Par-tez, la chan-ce vous sou-rit en-fin! Par-tez!
friends! For-wards! Dame For-tune is smil-ing once more! A-way!

L'istesso tempo.
al-lons, par-tons!
Now all a-way!
al-lons, par-tez!
Now all a-way!
al-lons, par-tons!
Now all a-way!
al-lons, par-tez!
Now all a-way!
al-lons, par-tons!
Now all a-way!
al-lons, par-tez!
Now all a-way!
al-lons, par-tons!
Now all a-way!
al-lons, par-tez!
Now all a-way!
et nous res-tons!
Here we shall stay!
et nous res-tons!
Here we shall stay!
L'istesso tempo.

Filina.
F.
Qui m'ai - me, me sui - ve! Et toi, Dieu des _ a -
Who loves _ me, will fol - low! And thou, oh god _ of
p
mours, Sois no - tre con - vi - ve; À ton ap - pel _ j'ac - cours! ah! ___
love, _ Do thou the fest - al hal - low! Thy call my heart doth move! ah! ___
Dieu des _ plai - sirs, des a - mours! ah! ___
God of _ plea - sure, god of _ love, ah, ___
À ta voix gaî - ment j'ac - cours, j'ac - cours tou - jours!
'Tis thy call my heart doth move, oh love! oh _ love!
f
sf
dim.
mf
Ah! ___ Qui m'ai - me, me sui - ve! Et _
Ah! ___ Who loves _ me, will fol - low! And

(1) If the cut be made, sing B♭ here instead of C.

La.
pour vous mieux re - ce - voir;
and your wel-come pre - pare;
Un splen-di - de sou -
There will be a fine
cresc.
ad lib.
per vous at - ten - dra ce soir!
sup - per wait - ing for you there!
Actresses.
Vi - vat!
Hur - rah!
Actors.
Vi - vat!
Hur - rah!
ff
Filina. (to Wilhelm.)
F.
Et vous, Mon - sieur, n'ê - tes - vous pas des
And you, Mon - sieur, will sure - ly not ig -
nô - - tres?
nore us?
(pause.)
p

F.
Grâce au galant seigneur qui, pour nous faire honneur,
Thanks to the courteous lord who has so kindly sent,
p
F.
Nous prête son carrosse, Nous allons, nous al-
to honor us, his carriage, We shall fare, we shall
F.
W.
dim.
Wilhelm. (with gallantry.)
lons voyager Comme en un jour de noce! Je vous dis au re-
fare to the feast As 'twere a day of marriage! Be sure, we meet a-
p
W.
voir! Vous me verrez ce soir; Je serai de la
gain! I shall be there at eve, For I will not for-
W.
(kissing her hand)
fête! Au revoir! au revoir! Vous me verrez ce
go it! By your leave! By your leave! I shall be there at

Filina.
F.
J'em-por - te cet es-poir, Nous nous ver-
I hope and will be-lieve, You will be
W.
soir!
eve!
Laertes. (aside.)
La.
p
À quoi bon la re - voir?
Where-fore see her a - gain?
F.
rons ce soir! A-dieu, mon cher po-è - - -
there at eve! Good bye, my gen-tle po - - -
W.
Ah! je veux la re-voir! O fol es - poir!
I shall see her a-gain. How fond! how fain!
La.
Quel fol es - poir Trou-ble de-jà son
Hope-less fol - ly, for the head or the
F.
te! Nous nous ver-rons ce soir! Au re-voir, mon cher-po-
et! You will be there at eve! So good-bye, my gen - tle
W.
Je se-rai de la fê - te, de la
No, I will not for - go it, not for-
La.
cœur, son cœur et sa
heart, did he on - ly
p

(taking Wilhelm's bouquet.)
F.
è - te!
po - et!
Et voi - ci mon bou-quet de fê - te!
These I'll take for my fest - al flow - ers!
W.
M.
Mignon.
f
fê - te!
go it!
Mon bou-
My bou-
La.
tê - te!
know it!
f
M.
W.
p
Wilhelm. (to Mignon.)
quet! mon bou - quet!
quet! my bou - quet!
Qu'as-tu
What is
p
Filina. (aside.)
Mignon. (to Wilhelm.)
F.
M.
Il m'a-do - re!
He a-dores me!
Vois,
See!
Laertes. (aside.)
W.
L.
donc!
wrong?
Il est pris!
He is caught!

(indicating Lothario)
M.
de mes pau-vres fleurs il n'a pas fait mé - pris! Il n'a
He did not des - pise the hum-ble flowrs I gave! He did
M.
W.
Wilhelm. (smiling.)
pas re - je - té mon bou - quet! lui! Par - don - ne!
not give a - way his bou - quet! No! For - give me!
sf
p
8
W.
M.
Mignon.
je ne l'ai pas of - fert, on me l'a pris. C'est bien! em - mè - ne -
I did not of - fer mine: Twas snatch'd a - way! Ah, well! Take me a -
8
M.
moi! Je t'ap - par - tiens! Or - don - ne!
long! I now am yours: com - mand me!
Wilhelm. (aside.)
W.
Oui, je veux la re - voir! Ô rêve! ô fol - es -
I shall see her a - gain! O dream, how fond, how

Filina.
Oui, voi-là pour ce
I shall see him at
Mignon. (aside.)
Il veut donc la re-voir!
He would see her a-gain!
poir! O char - man-te con - quê - - te!
fain! How de - light-ful a con - quest!
Laertes.
À quoi bon la re-voir? Quel a-mou-reux es-
Where-fore see her a-gain? His fond hope is in
cresc.
soir! Ma nou-vel-le con-quê-te, Je veux, je veux le re-voir!
eve! For my lat-est of con-quests I fain, I fain would a-chieve!
Mais quel est son es-poir?
But his hope is in vain.
O char-man-te con-quê - - te! quel es-poir!
How de-light-ful a con - quest! Ah! this eve!
poir! Il veut la re-voir!
vain! He'd see her a-gain!
f
p
pp

Mignon. (to the Gypsies.)
M.
Vous, dont j'ai par-ta-gé La honte et la mi-
You, whose partner I was in shame and de-gra-
sè - re, A-dieu!
da - tion, fare-well!
pp
(to the child, hanging a medallion about its neck.)
Toi, pauvre en-fant, sois un jour pro-té-
Thou, hap-less child, find pro-tec-tion some
gé Par cette hum-ble me-dail-le!
day in this hum-ble me-dal-lion!
(to Giarno.)
Et toi, dont la co-
And you whose an-gry

M.
lè - re M'a si sou-vent fait peur, hé-las! A-
hu - mor Made me so oft a - fraid, a - las! Fare-
(giving him her hand.)
dieu! Mi-gnon ne t'en veut pas!
well! Mi-gnon bears no ill-will!
Comedians. (at back)
mf
A - dieu! Phi - line, et bon vo-
Fare - well, Fi - li - na! luck at-
sf p cresc.
ya - ge!
tend you!
mf
Townsfolk and Peasants (at back)
A - dieu! la belle, et bon vo - ya - ge!
Fare-well! fare-well! may luck at-tend you!
Gypsies.
mf
A - dieu! Mi-gnon! et bon cou-
Fare-well! Mi-gnon! For-tune be-
sf p cresc.
f p cresc.

Lotario.
Lo.
J'en-tends au loin gronder l'o-
A-far I hear the tem-pest
Peasant-women and Actresses.
A-dieu! a-dieu! a-dieu!
Fare-well! fare-well! fare-well!
Actors.
A-dieu! a-dieu!
Fare-well! fare-well!
Townsfolk and Peasants.
A-dieu! a-dieu!
Fare-well! fare-well!
ra-ge! A-dieu! a-dieu!
friend you! Fare-well! fare-well!
La.
ra-ge, gron-der l'o-ra-
roar-ing, the tem-pest roar-

Lo.
ge!
ing!
Giarno.
G.
En route, _ a - mis, pli-ez ba - ga - - ge! La
A - way, _ ye friends! let all be go - - ing! Dame
En route, _ a - mis, pli-ons ba - ga - - ge! La
A - way, _ ye friends! let us be go - - ing! Dame
En route, _ a - mis, pli-ez ba - ga - - ge! La
A - way, _ ye friends! let all be go - - ing! Dame
En route, _ a - mis, pli-ons ba - ga - - ge! La
A - way, _ ye friends! let us be go - - ing! Dame
En route, _ a - mis, pli-ez ba - ga - - ge! La
A - way, _ ye friends! let all be go - - ing! Dame
En route, _ a - mis, pli-ons ba - ga - - ge! La
A - way, _ ye friends! let us be go - - ing! Dame
En route, _ a - mis, pli-ez ba - ga - - ge! La
A - way, _ ye friends! let all be go - - ing! Dame
En route, _ a - mis, pli-ons ba - ga - - ge! La
A - way, _ ye friends! let us be go - - ing! Dame
En route, _ a - mis, pli-ez ba - ga - - ge! La
A - way, _ ye friends! let all be go - - ing! Dame
En route, _ a - mis, pli-ez ba - ga - - ge! La
A - way, _ ye friends! let all be go - - ing! Dame

G.
chan - ce vous sou - rit en - fin! Ou - bli - ez vos re - pas d'au -
For - tune is smil - ing once more! Now a wel - come to ap - pe -
chan - ce nous sou - rit en - fin! Ou - bli - ons nos re - pas d'au -
For - tune is smil - ing once more! Now a wel - come to ap - pe -
chan - ce vous sou - rit en - fin! Ou - bli - ez vos re - pas d'au -
For - tune is smil - ing once more! Now a wel - come to ap - pe -
chan - ce nous sou - rit en - fin! Ou - bli - ons nos re - pas d'au -
For - tune is smil - ing once more! Now a wel - come to ap - pe -
chan - ce vous sou - rit en - fin! Ou - bli - ez vos re - pas d'au -
For - tune is smil - ing once more! Now a wel - come to ap - pe -
chan - ce nous sou - rit en - fin! Ou - bli - ons nos re - pas d'au -
For - tune is smil - ing once more! Now a wel - come to ap - pe -
chan - ce vous sou - rit en - fin! Ou - bli - ez vos re - pas d'au -
For - tune is smil - ing once more! Now a wel - come to ap - pe -
chan - ce nous sou - rit en - fin! Ou - bli - ons nos re - pas d'au -
For - tune is smil - ing once more! Now a wel - come to ap - pe -
chan - ce vous sou - rit en - fin! Ou - bli - ez vos re - pas d'au -
For - tune is smil - ing once more! Now a wel - come to ap - pe -
chan - ce vous sou - rit en - fin! Ou - bli -
For - tune is smil - ing once more! Now a
chan - ce vous sou - rit en - fin!
For - tune is smil - ing once more!
mf

G.
berge, Et sa-lu-ez, chapeau le-vé, Ce vieux cas-tel, ce vieux cas-
tite! Let us sa-lute, with hat in hand, This old — châ-teau, this old châ-
berge, Et sa-lu-ons, chapeau le-vé, Ce vieux cas-tel, ce vieux cas
tite! Let us sa-lute, with hat in hand, This old — châ-teau, this old châ
berge, Et sa-lu-ez, chapeau le-vé, Ce vieux cas-tel, ce vieux cas
tite! Let us sa-lute, with hat in hand, This old — châ-teau, this old châ
berge, Et sa-lu-ons, chapeau le-vé, Ce vieux cas-tel, ce vieux cas
tite! Let us sa-lute, with hat in hand, This old — châ-teau, this old châ
berge, Et sa-lu-ez, chapeau le-vé, Ce vieux cas-tel, ce vieux cas-
tite! Let us sa-lute, with hat in hand, This old — châ-teau, this old châ-
berge, Et sa-lu-ons, chapeau le-vé, Ce vieux cas-tel, ce vieux cas
tite! Let us sa-lute, with hat in hand, This old — châ-teau, this old châ
berge, Et sa-lu-ez, chapeau le-vé, Ce vieux cas-tèl, ce vieux cas
tite! Let us sa-lute, with hat in hand, This old — châ-teau, this old châ
berge, Et sa-lu-ons, chapeau le-vé, Ce vieux cas-tel, ce vieux cas
tite! Let us sa-lute, with hat in hand, This old — châ-teau, this old châ
berge, Et sa-lu-ez, chapeau le-vé, Ce vieux cas-tel, ce vieux cas-
tite! Let us sa-lute, with hat in hand, This old — châ-teau, this old châ-
ez vos re-pas d'au-ber-ge, Sa-lu-ez Ce vieux cas-tel, ce vieux cas
welcome to ap-pe-tite! ——— And sa-lute This old — châ-teau, this old châ

Allegro, tempo di Valzer.
Filina.
F.
Ah! a - mis, sa - lu - ez, chapeau le - vé, A - mis, sa - lu - ez ce vieux cas-
Ah! Friends all, sa - lute it, with hat in hand, friends all, sa - lute it, this old châ-
Mignon.
M.
Ah! ah! je suis li - bre, oui, libre en - fin! Un dé - fenseur m'a ten - du la
Ah! ah! I am free now, yes, free at last! For my de - fend - er will hold me
Wilh.
W.
Ah! mon cœur, je le crois, est pris en - fin! Je m'a - ban - don - ne à mon des-
Ah! my heart, I feel it, is caught at last! I yield to Fortune, the die is
Laertes.
La.
Ah! a - mis, sa - lu - ez, chapeau le - vé, A - mis, sa - lu - ez ce vieux cas-
Ah! Friends all, sa - lute it, with hat in hand, friends all, sa - lute it, this old châ-
Loth.
Lo.
Ah! sois maudit, cru - el des - tin! Je veux la trouver en-
Ah! Fate all hope ev - er doth blast! Oh, might I find her at
Giarno.
G.
tel, sa - lu - ez, chapeau le - vé, sa - lu - ez ce vieux cas-
teau! Sa - lute it, with hat in hand, sa - lute it, this old châ-
Chorus.
tel, a - mis, sa - {lu - ons, lu - ez,} chapeau le - vé, A - mis, sa - {lu - ons lu - ez} ce vieux cas-
teau! Ye friends, sa - lute it, with hat in hand, ye friends, sa - lute it, this old châ-
tel, sa - {lu - ons, lu - ez,} chapeau le - vé, sa - {lu - ons lu - ez} ce vieux cas-
teau! Sa - lute it, with hat in hand, sa - lute it, this old châ-
Allegro, tempo di Valzer. 𝅗𝅥.=80

F.
tel, où l'on hé - ber - ge Les his - tri - ons sur_ le pa - vé,
teau, let all sa - lute it, this old châ - teau, where co - me-dians
M.
main Ah! je suis li - bre, oui, libre en - fin! Mon_ cœur bé - nit
fast! Ah, I am free now, yes, free at last! Blest be For - tune!
W.
tin! Mon cœur, je le crois, est pris en - fin! Je m'a - ban - don - ne
cast! My heart, I feel it, is caught at last! I yield to For - tune,
La.
tel, où l'on hé - ber - ge Les his - tri - ons sur_ le pa - vé,
teau, let all sa - lute it, this old châ - teau, where co - me-dians
Lo.
fin! Sois mau-dit, cru - el des - tin! Je veux la
last! Fate all hope ev - er doth blast! Oh, might I
G.
tel, Re - fu - ge des his - tri - ons sur le pa - vé,
teau! Sa - lute it, this old châ - teau, where co - me-dians
tel, où l'on hé - ber - ge Les his - tri - ons sur_ le pa - vé,
teau! Let all sa - lute it, this old châ - teau, where co - me-dians
tel, Re - fu - ge des his - tri - ons sur le pa - vé,
teau, sa - lute it, this old châ - teau, where co - me-dians

F.
ff
tr
sur le pa-vé! Ah! ah!
they now in-vite! Ah! ah!
M.
le — des-tin! Ah! un dé - fen-
woe_ is past! Ah! for my de-
W.
à mon des-tin! Ah! ah!
the die is cast! Ah! ah!
La.
sur le pa-vé! Ah! a-mis, pliez ba-ga - ge!
they now in-vite! Ah! ye friends, away be go - ing!
Lo.
trou-ver en-fin! Ah! Ah! j'en-tends l'o-
find her at last! Ah! Ah! I hear the
G.
sur le pa-vé! Ah! a-mis, pliez ba-ga - ge!
they now in-vite! Ah! ye friends, away be go - ing!
sur le pa-vé! Ah! Ah! le jo-li vo-
they now in-vite! Ah! Ah, what a mer-ry
sur le pa-vé! Ah! a-mis, {plions / pliez} ba-ga - ge,
they now in-vite! Ah! ye friends, away be go ing!

F.
Que
May
M.
seur — m'a — ten - du — la main,
fend - er now — will hold me fast!
Sa
Ah!
W.
Res -
To
La.
A - mis, pliez ba - ga - ge! par-tons, oui, par-tons!
ye friends, away be go - ing, a - way, ay, a - way!
Que
May
Lo.
ra - ge! Ah! — par - tons, par - tons!
tem - pest! Ah! — a - way, a - way!
J'en -
I
G.
A - mis, pliez ba - ga - ge! par-tez, oui, par-tez!
ye friends, away be go - ing, a - way, ay, a - way!
Que
May
ya - ge! A - mis, {par-tons! par-tez!} oui! {par-tons! par-tez!}
jour - ney! Friends all, a - way, ay, a - way!
Que
May
A - mis, {plions pli-ez} ba - ga - ge {par - tons! par - tez!} {par - tons! par - tez!}
Ye friends, away be go - ing, a - way, a - way!
Que
May

F.
la — gaî - té soit du vo - ya - - - - -
ev - 'ry joy ev-er at - tend
M.
voix m'a ren - du le cou - ra - ge!
his voice has giv'n me new cour - age!
W.
ter i - ci se - rait plus sa - ge!
stay here would be far more pru - dent!
La.
la gaî - té soit du vo - ya - ge!
all joy for ev - er at - tend us!
Lo.
tends au loin gron - der l'o - ra - ge!
hear a - far the tem - pest roar - ing!
G.
la gaî - té soit du vo - ya - ge!
all joy for ev - er at - tend you!
la — gaî - te soit du vo - ya - - - - ge!
ev - 'ry joy ev-er at - tend us! you!
la gaî - té soit du vo - ya - ge!
all joy for ev - er at - tend — us! you!
la gaî - té soit du vo - ya - ge!
all joy for ev - er at - tend — us! you!

F.
-ge! Ah!
us! Ah!

Giarno.
G.
p
Ah! quel heu-reux des-tin!
What a for-tu-nate day!

p
Ah! quel heu-reux des - tin!
What a for-tu-nate day!

p
Ah! quel heu-reux des - tin!
What a for-tu-nate day!

p

p

F.
f
Ah!
Ah!

G.
Ah! quel heureux des-tin!
What a for-tu-nate day!
f
Oui,
Yes,

Ah! quel heureux des - tin!
What a for-tu-nate day!
f
Oui,
Yes,

Ah! quel heureux des tin!
What a for-tu-nate day!
f
Oui,
Yes,

f

f

f

Filina.
F.
ah! ah! quel heu-reux des-tin! Ah!
ah! what a for-tu-nate day! Ah!
Mignon.
M.
Ah! ah! je suis libre en-fin! Ah! ah! je
Ah! I am free now, at last! Ah! I am
Wilhelm.
W.
Mais je m'a-ban-donne à mon des-tin. À la re-voir mon
To Fate I yield me, the die is cast! I can-not bid her
Laertes.
La.
La chance, a-mis, nous sou-rit en-fin! A-mis, par-tons! pli-
Dame For-tune now is smil-ing once more! A-way, ye friends, a-
Lothario.
Lo.
Ah! mau-dit, mau-dit soit le des-tin! Je veux la re-trou-
Ah! Fate, Fate doth my hope ev-er blast! Oh, might I find her
Giarno.
G.
La chance, a-mis, vous sou-rit en-fin! A-mis, par-tez! pli-
Dame For-tune now is smil-ing once more! A-way, ye friends, a-
oui, La chance, a-mis, nous vous sou-rit en-fin! A-mis, pli- pli-
yes! Dame For-tune now is smil-ing once more! A-way, ye
oui, La chance, a-mis, nous vous sou-rit en-fin! A-mis, par-tons! par-tez! pli- pli-
yes! Dame For-tune now is smil-ing once more! A-way, ye friends, a-

F.
par - tons!
A - way!
M.
suis libre en - fin! en - fin!
free now, at last! at last!
W.
cœur s'en-gage, Il faut ai-mer en - fin!
now fare-well, my heart must love at last!
La.
ez bagage; A-mis, par-tons! par - tons!
way, ye friends! A-way! a-way! a - way!
Lo.
ver en-fin! Par-tons! par-tons! par - tons!
now, at last! A-way! a-way! a - way!
G.
ez ba-gage, A-mis, par-tez! par - tez!
way, ye friends! A-way! a way! a - way!
-ons
-ez
ba - ga - ge!
par - tons!
par - tez!
friends, be go - ing! a - way!
ons
ez
ba-gage! A-mis,
par-tons!
par-tez!
par - tons!
par - tez!
way, be-gone! A-way, ye friends, a - way!

8
8
8
End of Act I.

Act II.

Nº 7. Recit.: "A merveille! J'en ris d'avance!"

Entr'acte.

1st Tableau. An elegant dressing-room; R. H., a window, L. H., a fireplace and mantel. Luxurious articles of toilet; sofas, easy-chairs, etc.

A(2) See at the end of this score, in the Supplement, the new air of Filina *(ad lib.)* sung by Mme. Volpini in London.

Filina (seated before her toilet-table, on which are letters and bouquets).

(enters.)
la! la la la la la la la la, la! la la la
Filina.
C'est La-
'Tis La-
la la la, la la la la la la la la!
cresc.
f
f
Allegro moderato
Recit.
ër-te!
er-tes! (with a majestic air.)
(on the threshold.)
Oui, mon
Yes, my
p
Cor-bleu!.. les somptu-eux lam-bris! C'est i - ci qu'on vous lo - ge?
My soul! What a superb dis - play! Is it here you are quarter'd?
Allegro moderato.
p
cher, la Baronne me prê - te son boudoir.
dear, 'tis the Baroness lends me her boudoir.
(slily.)
Et le Baron, mi-gnon-ne, en a gar-dé la
And the Baron, my sweet one, has he retain'd the

*) Here the transposition of the Madrigal into $B\flat$ may be effected.

Nº 8. "Belle, ayez pitié de nous."

Madrigal.

più largamente
flè-ches meur-tri-è - res Du Dieu, du Dieu qui nous bles - se
wan-ton ar-rows slay - ing, Of the god, the god who doth wound us
a tempo
tous! Et lon la la! et lon lon la! lan-dé-ri-dé-ra, lan-dé-ri-dé-
all! Et lon la la! et lon lon la! lan-dé-ri-dé-ra, lan-dé-ri-dé-
ra, et lon lon la! lan-dé-ri-dé - ra!
ra, et lon lon la, lan-dé-ri-dé - ra!
(last measure of Madrigal in B♭.)
Laertes (with a pirouette).
Voi-là!
So-ho!
Moderato.
Recit.
Filina (mockingly).
Fort bien! on croit en-
Well sung! Your strain re-
(last measure of Madrigal in G.)
Laertes (with a pirouette).
Voi-là!
So-ho!
Moderato.
Recit.
Filina (mockingly).
Fort bien! on croit en-
Well sung! Your strain re-

F.
tendre, Je vous jure, le jeune Frédéric! Comment n'est-il pas ici?
minds me, I assure you, of Fred-e-rick himself! Laertes. But wherefore is he not here?
L.
Merci!
How kind!
a tempo
cresc.
Il viendra! J'en suis sûre, il est en route, il vient...
He will come! I am certain! He's on the way now, he's near_
(slily.)
Et Wilhelm? Croyez-vous?
And Wilhelm? Are you sure!
p
a tempo
W.
Wilhelm (appears on the threshold).
f
Belle Philine!
Lovely Filina!
Et le voici!
and here he is!
cresc.
(going to meet him.)
Laertes.
Recit.
Bon! très bien! Je vais voir là-
Ha! 'tis well! I shall go and

L.
bas si tout s'apprête! Le Son-ge d'u-ne nuit d'é - té Doit fai-re les frais de la
see that all is ready! The play is "A Midsummer Night's Dream," and 'twill be our best enter -
fê - te! C'est d'un nommé Shaeks-pea - re, un as-sez bon po - è - te!
tain-ment; 'tis by a man call'd Shakespeare, a fair-ly clev-er po - et!
p
(indicating Filina.)
(emphatically.)
f
Et de Ti - ta - ni - a vous se-rez en-chan - té! A bien -
And you will fall in love with Ti - ta - nia, I know! I'll re -
f
p
tôt, cher monsieur! A - dieu, ma tou-te bel - le! Je vous lais-se a-vec
tire, with your leave! Fare-well, love-ly Fi - li - na! Now I leave you with
f
largamente
(to Wilhelm.)
(stopping near door at back.)
lui, Je vous laisse a-vec el - le.
him: and with her I shall leave you!
f

Moderato.
Filina.
F.
Mignon?
Mignon?
Wilhelm.
W.
C'est Mi - gnon!
'Tis Mi - gnon!
El - le n'a
Poor child, she
L.
Mais qui donc se tient là?
But who else is there here?
Quoi?
What?
Moderato. (♩= 104)
pp
pas vou-lu se sé-pa-rer de moi!..
could not bear to go a-way from me!
Faut-il l'ap-pe-ler?
Shall I call her in?
Soit!
Yes!
(Wilhelm goes toward back, and calls:)
Mignon!
Mignon!
Mignon (appears, attired as a page).
W.
M.
Que veux - tu, maî - tre?
What's your will, mas - ter?
(smiling)
Eh! mais vrai -
Ah, real - ly,

Recit.
F.
ment, on a peine à la re-con-naî - tre!
now! one can hard-ly re - cog - nize her!
Approche et réchauf-fe-
Come nearer, that you may get
rit.
smorzando
(mockingly.)
toi! Tu nous danse - ras en - sui - te la dan - se des oeufs!
warm; and af-terward you shall dance us your dance on the eggs!
M.
(Mignon starts.)
L.
Laertes (aside.)
Je
A
Filina.
Plaît - il?
What's that?
crois qu'un o-rage est dans l'air!
tem - pest is brewing, I think!
Rien! je vous quit - te!
Nothing! I am go - ing!
(exit Laertes.)

Nº 9. "Plus de soucis, Mignon!"

Trio.

F. chants! Que de bon-tés! Quels soins tou-chants! Que de bon-
kind! What mov-ing care! How ver-y kind! What mov-ing

(laughing)

F. tés! Ah! ah ah ah ah ah ah! per-met-tez-moï de
care! Ah! ah ah ah ah ah ah! I real-ly can't help

F. ri-re, per-met-tez-moi de ri-re De ce beau dé-vou-
laugh-ing, I real-ly can't help laugh-ing At de-vo-tion so

F. ment! Ah ah ah ah ah ah!
rare!

Mignon (aside).

M. Hé-las! Qu'a-t-el-le à ri-re? Cruel a-mu-se-
A-las, why is she laugh-ing? She's cru-el as she's

M. F. ment! Filina. Ah ah ah ah ah ah!
fair!

Wilhelm (to Filina).

W. Vous fai-tes bien de ri-re, Vo-tre rire est char-
'Tis well that you are laugh-ing, 'Tis de-light-ful to

Mignon.
W.
M.
mant. Hé-las! qu'at-elle à ri-re? Cru-el a-mu-se-
hear! A-las! why is she laugh-ing? She's cru-el as she's
fp
p
f
3
F.
Ah ah ah ah ah ah!
Ah! mon cher, je vous ad-
Ah, my dear, how I ad-
M.
ment!
fair!
mi-re! C'est tout à fait char-mant! Ah! Je vous admire you! 'Tis al-to-geth-er-rare! Ah! how I ad-
8
mi-re! Ah! c'est char-mant! Au lieu d'ê-tre ser-
mire you! Ah! it is rare! In-stead of be-ing
tr
vi par vo-tre jeu-ne pa-ge, C'est vous qui le ser-
serv'd by your young man in wait-ing, it is on him you

Wilhelm.
F.
W.
vez! Près de vous! à vos pieds J'accep-te-rais, si vous vou-liez,
wait! Near to you, at your feet, I would ac-cept! if 'twere your will,
Filina.
p
Un plus doux ser-va-ge. Vraiment!
a far sweet-er ser-vice! In-deed!
(pointing to a candle on the mantel)
Ap-por-tez donc ce flambeau par i-ci!
Then, pray you, fetch yonder can-dle this way!
Wilhelm.
(bringing it)
mf
Je me fais votre es-cla-ve, Ordonnez! me voi-
As your slave I o-bey you! Say your will! I am
sf
f
p
Filina.
Recit.
ci! Merci! Mon coiffeur m'a, ce soir, in-di-gnement coif-fé-e...
here! Thank you! Tho' my hairdresser made a fright of me this eve-ning,

largamente
Mais vous al-lez me voir dans la ro-be de fé - e!
you shall behold me soon in my fai - ry cos - tume!
sf
ff
Variant.
Ah!
dim.
Ah!
dim. e rit.
Allegretto. (♩. = 72)
dol.
Je crois en-
Hith-er-ward
p
ten-dre Les doux com-pli-ments, Et la voix ten-dre De vingt a-
hie-ing, Gal-lant-ly vy-ing, Of lov-ers sigh-ing A score be-
mants. Cha-cun m'ad-mi-re, Jeu-nes et vieux, Cha-cun sou-
hold! All me ad-mir-ing, Or young they, or old; All are as-
pi-re Pour mes beaux yeux.
pir-ing My heart to-hold!
Wilhelm.
J'ad-mi-re l'é-clat de vos
How bright of thine eyes ev-'ry
mf
F.
W.

W.
yeux! Je suis ra - vi, char-mé d'en - ten - dre Cet - te
ray! I am en - rav - ish'd by their splen - dor, By thy
mf
dim.
voix a - mou - reuse_ et ten - dre, Ce - ri - re moqueur et joy -
voice so di - vine - ly ten - der, Thy laughter so mock-ing and
Filina.
p
Ah! Ah! Ah!
dim.
Mignon. (aside)
M.
N'é - cou - tons pas! fer - mons les yeux! (pretends to be asleep)
I may not hear! I will not see!
eux.
gay!
F.
Je crois en - ten - dre Les_doux com - pli - ments, Et_la voix
Hith - er - ward hie - ing, Gal_- lant - ly vy - ing, Of_lov - ers
Ah! j'ad - mi - re l'éclat, l'é -
Ah! how bright of your eyes, how

F.
ten - dre De vingt a - mants! Cha - cun m'ad -
sigh - ing A score be - hold! All me ad -
M.
Mignon.
Je ne veux rien en - ten - dre!
I will no lon - ger hear them!
W.
clat de vos beaux yeux!
bright is ev - 'ry ray!
mi - re, Jeu - nes et vieux, Cha - cun
mir - ing, Or young or old, All are
N'é - cou - tons pas!
I may not hear!
rit.
segue
sou - pi - re Pour mes beaux yeux! Ah cha - cun sou -
a - spir - ing My heart to hold! Ay! All are a -
pi - re Pour mes beaux yeux! Ah! cha - cun sou -
spir - ing My heart to hold! Ah! All are a -
risoluto

cresc. — **Wilhelm.** *f*

F. W.

pi - re_ Pour mes_ beaux yeux! Bel - le Phi -
spir - ing_ My_ heart_ to hold! Love - ly Fi

cresc. *f* *f*

W.

line! ai - ma - ble enchan - te - res - - se!
li - - na! Beau - ti - ful en - chant - - ress!

(passionately) *p*

W.

Ah! Vos_ doux re - gards_ et
Ah! Your_ ten - der gaze,_ and

p

W.

vos at - traits vain - queurs À_ vo - tre
all your con - qu'ring charms, un - to your

W.

char_ en - chaî - nent tous les
car_ do fet - ter ev - - 'ry

Filina. (showing her bracelet)
p
F.
Ce bra-ce-let du prince est charmant!
This bracelet from the Prince is su-perb!
W.
p
cœurs! Autour de vous tout sou-rit et s'empres- - se! On vous
heart! Where'er you go, all are smiles, all would serve you! How they
W.
cresc.
fête, on vous aime, on vous a-do- -re! Hé-las! Hé-las!
pet, how they love, how they a-dore you! Ah me! Ah me!
W.
dim.
pour-quoi n'aimez- -vous pas, ai-mable
Ah, why have you no heart, you beau- - -
pp
F.
Filina.
p
Il est char-mant! n'est-ce pas?
It is su-perb, is it not?
W.
en-chan- -te-res- -se? Ah!
- ti-ful en-chant-ress? Ah!
dim.

W.
Ah! Phili - ne, pour-quoi n'aimez-vous pas?
Ah, Fi-li - na, ah, why have you no heart?
f
dim.
Filina.
F.
Au ba-ron il faut qu'on vous pré-sen - te.
To the Ba - ron you must be pre-sent - ed!
(pointing at Mignon)
Wilhelm.
Philine! un mot en-
Fi - li - na! but a
p
Par-lez plus bas! Notre hô - te nous at - tend! Of-frez-moi vo-tre
Speak not so loud! Our host a-waits us now! Please to give me your
co - re un mot!
word, one word!
colla parte
(giving him her hand)
bras!
arm!
Al-lons! J'ai l'â - me complai-
Oh well! I can not be too
Wilhelm.
Quoi! sans ré-pon - - dre?
What! still no an - - swer?

F.
(aside)
p
san - te!
cru - el!
Je sa-vais bien qu'el-le ne dormait pas.
I knew quite well that she was not a-sleep!
W.
O Philine, ô co
O Fi-li - na, a-
f
F.
f a tempo
La la la, la la,
la la, la la,
W.
f riten.
quette a - do - ra - ble, en-i - vran-te!
dor-a - ble, charm-ing co-quette!
a tempo
riten.
f
p
Variant
F.
dim.
la la, la la, la la, la la!
W.
mf
Ah!
Ah!
sf
cresc.
ff

F.
W.
La la, la la, la la, la la! tou-
For
Par pi tié daignez, dai-gnez m'en-
Ah, in pit - y deign, ah deign to
p
sf
tr
dim.
jours! ah! tou-jours!
aye! ah! for aye!
Mignon.
M.
p
De cet en-tre-tien doux et
Ah, this ten-der scene, and so
ten-dre!
hear me!
Un seul re-gard de vos doux yeux,
One-glance a-lone from your sweet eyes,
Cha-cun m'ad-mi-re!
All me ad-miring,
ten - dre
near them!
Je ne veux rien en-ten - dre!
I will no longer hear them!
Un mot de cet-te voix, cet-te voix ten - dre,
On - ly a word from your voice, ah, so ten - der!

F.
Jeu-nes et vieux, Cha-cun sou-pi-re Pour mes beaux yeux! oui!
Or young or old; All are a-spir-ing My heart to hold! Ay!
W.
Un mot de cet - te voix,
One word of thy dear voice,
W.
cet - te voix ten-dre En-ivre, en - i - vre mon cœur a - mou-
thy voice so ten-der, rav-ish-es, rav-ish-es my love - ing
cresc.
dim.
Filina.
F.
Ah!
Ah!
W.
reux!
heart!
F.
Ah!
Ah!
Mignon.
M.
Non, je ne veux rien en - ten -
Ah! no lon-ger will I hear
W.
Ah! Par pi-tié dai - gnez m'en-
Ah! Ah, in pit - y deign to

cresc.
pp
dre! N'é-cou-tons pas!
them! I will not hear!
Pour dor-mir,
Ah, to sleep,
pour dor-mir,
ah, to sleep
ten- dre!
hear me!
Un seul mot,
But a word,
un re-
but a
cresc.
pp
cresc.
ah! je fais
I shall still
de mon mieux!
try my best!
Pour dor-mir,
Ah, to sleep
gard
glance
de vos yeux
of thine eyes
En - i - vre mon
doth rav - ish my
cresc.
pp
f
Ah!
Ah!
oui, je fais
I shall still
de mon mieux!
try my best!
mf
cœur a - mou-reux!
fond, lov - ing heart!
Ah! répons, de
Ah! re-ply, I
pp

F.
dim.
p
Ah!
Ah!
W.
grâ - ce, Phi - li - ne, ré - ponds! ah! ré - ponds - moi!
pray __ thee, Fi - li - na! re - ply! ah, answer me!
dim.
F.
dim.
pp
rit.
ah!
ah!
W.
p
Un __ seul mot ré - pon - dez de grâ - ce
But __ a word! Ah, re - ply, I pray thee,
rit.
rit.
a tempo
(exeunt Filina and Wilhelm)
F.
f
ah! ah!
ah! ah!
M.
f
Ah! fai - sons de mon mieux.
Ah! I shall try my best!
a tempo
W.
f
À mon cœur a - mou - reux!
Pit - y my lov - ing heart.
ff a tempo
ff
p

dim.
pp
Moderato.
Mignon. (alone)
Recit. (sadly)
M.
Me voi-là seu-le, hé-las! dé-jà Meis-ter m'ou-
I am a - lone now; A-las! al-read-y he for-
bli-e... Qu'im-por-te! il a com-blé mes vœux! Le suivre et le ser-
gets me! What mat-ter! He grant-ed my de-sire! To fol-low and to
un poco animato
p
vir, C'est tout ce que je veux. Al-lons! pleu-rer se-rait fo-
serve Is all I can re-quire. No tears! What vain fol-ly be-
f
p
li-e... Non! non!... à tout je me sou-mets. Ne pleu-rons
sets me! No! no! To all I will sub-mit; I'll weep no
mf
(with decision)
f

Allegro moderato.
(looking around her)
M.
mf
plus!
more!
La splen-di-de de-meu-re! Je n'ai ja-
What an el-e-gant dwelling! No-thing so
dim.
mais rien vu de pa-reil, non, ja-mais! si ce n'est en rê-ve...
fine I ev-er have seen, no, in-deed! if 'twere not while dream-ing.
p
Un poco più vivace.
(stopping before the toilet-table)
poco
Ah! c'est là que tout à l'heu-re en sou-ri-ant a son mi-
Ah! but now, here she was stand-ing, smil-ing-ly gaz-ing at her
cresc.
(ingenuously)
roir Elle é-cou-tait Meis-ter! Je ne vou-lais rien
glass, list'-ning to Meis-ter here! I did not wish to
voir, je ne vou-lais rien en-ten-dre! Hé-las!
see, I tried to hear them no lon-ger! A-las!

*) If the Styrienne is to be sung in E minor, skip to the sign ⊕ on next page.

animandosi
cresc.
M.
Ma pâ-leur dis-pa-raît dé-jà! Mon teint s'a-
Now my pal-lor's al-read-y gone! My cheeks are
ni-me. fard qui la rend bel-le. Eh bien!
glow-ing! paint that makes her love-ly! O-ho!
(Continue with the Styrienne in D minor)
si j'es-sa-yais de me far-der aus - si?
sup-pose I try to paint my-self as well!
Allegretto. (♩. = 72)
(tries to rouge herself)
animandosi
cresc.
Ma pâ-leur dis-pa-rait dé-jà! mon teint s'a-ni-me.
Now my pal-lor's al-read-y gone! my cheeks are glow-ing!
(Continue with the Styrienne in E minor)

Nº 10. "Je connais un pauvre enfant."

Styrienne.(1)

(1) The Styrienne may be transposed a tone higher, that is, into E minor.

M.
Ah!
Ah!
(admiring herself in the glass.)
Est-ce bien Mignon,
Can it be Mignon?
est-ce bien Mi-gnon que voi-là?
Can it be Mi-gnon whom I see?
Ah!
Ah!
Est-ce bien Mi-gnon?
Can it be Mi-gnon?
Ta la!
Ta la!
Tempo I.
Un beau jour, tout tri-om-phant, Tout
One fine day, sore-ly be-guil'd, Tri-
secco
più ritenuto

M.
rall.
fier de son stra-ta-gè-me,_ Pour plai-re au maî-tre qu'il ai-
um-phant wait-ed the maid-en,_ Her be-lov-ed mas-ter to glad-
pp
Più animato
f
me... Ah!_ la folle his-toi-re!
den_ Ah!_ Sure-ly 'tis fol-ly!
f
dim.
p
en vain je m'en dé-fends,_ Je me trouve bien mieux, je ne suis plus la
Howe'er I would re-frain,_ I fear I'm growing vain!_ Who am I, on a
dim.
rit. a tempo
p
mê-me! Ah! Ah! la la_ la la ta-la la!_ tra la! la_ la la!
sud-den?
f
rit. mf a tempo
gnon?
gnon?
p
mf
p
Ah! la la_ la la ta-la la_ Ah!_ Est-ce bien Mi-gnon?_
Can it be Mi-gnon?_
p
mf
p

M.
ta la la!
mezza voce con amabilità
La la la la la la la la
la la ah! la la!
dim.
Est-ce bien Mi-gnon? est-ce bien Mi-gnon? est-ce bien Mignon que voi-
Can it be Mi-gnon? Can it be Mi-gnon? Can it be Mignon whom I
là?
see?
La la la la la la la!

p
sf
dim.
poco rit.
M.
ah!
col canto
sf
a piacere
f
ah!
p
f
p
cresc.
Ah!
a tempo
f
p
tra la la la la!
Est - ce moi? est-ce bien Mi-
Is it I? Can it be Mi-
string. e cresc.
gnon que voi- là? la la la la ah!
gnon whom I see?
8
ff

Variant.
M.
Lo stesso movimento.
(gaily.)
Non! non! ce n'est plus moi!
No, no! It is not I!
(sadly.)
Mais quoi! ce n'est pas el - le!
But ah! 'tis not Fi - li - na!
Elle a d'au - tres se-crets en - cor pour ê - tre
She knows of ways un-known to me, to make her
(goes to open the door of the dressing-room.)
bel - le.
love - ly.

(In case the Rondo-Gavotte sung by Mme Trebelli-Bettini is executed, the 9 measures of recitative which precede the entrance of Wilhelm must be omitted.)

(with indignation.)
Fr.
ci! Quoi! mon oncle a logé Phi-li-ne chez ma tan-
here! What my un-cle has lodg'd Fi-li-na in my aunt's
Wilhelm (partly opening door at back). Frederick. Wilhelm (enters without seeing Frederick.)
Fr. W.
te? Mi-gnon! Hein? J'ai pro-mis de me sé-pa-rer
rooms? Mi-gnon! Ha! I a-greed up-on our se-pa-
(noticing Frederick.) Frederick (aside.)
W. Fr.
d'el-le... ah! quel-qu'un! N'est-ce pas le ga-lant de tan-
ra-tion— ah! who's here? Is it not the gal-lant whom I
(saluting.)
W.
C'est je crois le jeu-ne sot de l'au-ber-ge. Mon-
'Tis that fool-ish boy, I think, of the tav-ern. Mon-
Fr.
tôt? Monsieur!
saw? Monsieur!
Frederick.
W. Fr.
sieur! Je suis peut-être in-dis-cret, mais comment vous trou-vez-vous i-
sieur! Tho' I ap-pear in-dis-creet, pray in-form me how 'tis you are

Wilhelm.
Frederick.
Fr.
W.
ci? Et vous-mê-me, Mon-sieur? Moi! c'est par la fe-
here? And your-self, Mon-sieur? I? It was thro' the
Wilhelm (laughing.)
nê-tre que je suis en-tré. Dieu mer-ci! moi, J'y suis en-tré par la
win-dow that I en-ter'd in! Heav'n be prais'd, I, I en-ter'd in by the
(still calmly.)
por-te. J'en suis aus-si!
door-way! I am the same!
(more warmly.)
Je suis de ses a-mis, Monsieur! Mais moi, je
I am a friend of hers, Monsieur! But I, I
Eh bien! moi, je l'a-do-re!
As for me, I a-dore her!
l'ai-me! En sor-te que nous sommes ri-
love her! And there-fore we are ri-vals, it

W.
p
Il paraît!
So it seems!
Fr.
f
vaux...
seems.
Sa-vez-vous en quel pas dan-gereux vo-tre amour se ha-
Do you know in what dan-ger-ous wa-ters your love has ad-
f
(coolly.)
Oui, je crois le sa-voir!
Yes, I think that I know!
mf
Plaît-il?
What now!
(draws.)
Più animato.
sar-de?
ven-tured?
Bien! il suf-fit! en gar-de! En
Good! 'Tis enough! De-fend you! De-
Quel cour-roux!
What a rage!
gar-de!
fend you!
Vous vous bat-trez bien, j'i-ma-gi-ne?
You know how to fight, I i-ma-gine!
Quoi! chez Phi-li-ne?
What? in her cham-ber?
Chez Phi-li-ne! C'est plus o-ri-gi-
In her cham-ber! 'tis more o-ri-gi-
cresc.

M.
Battons-nous!
Let us fight!
Fr.
nal!
nal!
Battons-nous!
Let us fight!
(crossing swords.)
(Mignon comes from dressing-room, attired in one of Filina's dresses.)
Mignon (throwing herself between them.)
M.
Fr.
Ah! Meis-ter! Dieu!
Ah! no more! Heav'ns!
Frederick.
Mi-gnon? que si-gni-
Mi-gnon? What's this, I
W.
Wilhelm.
Mignon!
Mignon!
(mockingly, and sheathing his sword.)
Fr.
fi-e? Mais voi-là, si je m'en sou-viens, les a-tours de Phi-
won-der? Ah! I see! if I am not wrong, the garments of Fi-
Wilhelm (seriously.)
W.
Monsieur!
Monsieur!
(laughing.)
Fr.
li-ne! Ah! ah! ah! ah! ah! ah! Bien! je ne veux pas ô-ter la
li-na! Ha ha ha ha ha ha! Well! I sure-ly do not care to

poco più f
Fr.
vi-e à cette en-fant pour vous per-cer le cœur! Nous nous re-ver-
kill her, this pret-ty child, mere-ly to break your heart! We shall meet a-
Allegro moderato.
(exit laughing.)
Recit.
Wilhelm
(sternly.)
Fr.
W.
rons! Ser-vi-teur!
gain! Sir, your servant!
Toi, Mi-
You, Mi-
Mignon.
W.
M.
gnon, toi sous ces ha-bits! Par-don-ne! Je suis en fau-te, je le
gnon? you, in this at-tire? Forgive me! It was not proper, that I
M.
sais! Je n'ai pu ré-sis-ter, et j'ai cru que per-son-ne ne me ver-
know! But I could not re-sist, and I thought there was no one near me to
Wilhelm.
M.
W.
rait. Quel est ce caprice in-sen-sé? Deviens-tu fol-le? Alors quittons-
see! What is this in-sensate ca-price? Are you de-mented? If so, let us

un poco rit.
M.
W.
Tu me chas-ses?
You dis-miss me?
(more kindly.)
nous!
part!
Non! non! je ne te chas-se pas!
No, no! I shall not send you off!
sf
p
Même je dois te ren-dre grâ-ces Du tendre mouve-ment qui te jet-te en mes
Ra-ther to you all thanks I ren-der, That in de-vo-tion ten-der You fly in-to my
bras Pour me sau-ver et me dé-fen-dre! Mais je commence à com-
arms, To be my sav-ior and de-fend-er! But I be-gin to per-
mf
pren-dre Que je ne puis au-près de moi Te gar-der, pauvre en-
ceive it, that you no lon-ger may re-main my com-pan-ion, poor
Mignon.
Pour-quoi?
And why?
fant!
child!
Pour-quoi?
And why?
Par-ce-que un pa-reil
'Tis be-cause such a
p

W.
page Ne peut ser-vir un gar-çon de mon â - ge; Je l'ou-bli -
page Can-not well serve a young man of my age; I had for -
Mignon.
W.
M.
ais, tu me l'as rap-pe - lé! Hé-las! il m'a-vait sem -
got: Now you call it to mind! A - las! it ap-pear'd to
M.
blé... Rien!.. J'é-tais fol-le... oh la ro-be mau-di-te Qui m'en-lai -
me Nothing! I was cra-zy! Oh, accurs'd be the garment that made me
W.
Quoi donc?
Say on!
M.
dit en-cor à tes yeux!
yet more ug - ly to you!
W.
Non, vrai - ment! ai - je dit ce - la? Mais va
No, in - deed! Did I tell you that? But go

(sadly.) Moderato ritenuto.

M. C'est el - le as-su-rément qui vous a conseil - lé de me chasser!
'Twas she, I feel assur'd, it was she who ad - vis'd you to send me off!

W. vi - te! Phi-li - ne peut ve-nir.
quickly! Fi - li - na may re-turn.

Moderato ritenuto.

f *p*

W. É - cou - te! Je ne puis te gar-der, Que di - rait - on?
Do list-en! You can nev - er remain: what would be said?

cresc.

(bitterly.)

M. Sans dou - te.
No ques - tion!

W. D'ail - leurs je te l'ai dit, je ne te chas - se pas!
Be - sides, as I have said, I shall not send you off!

dim.

(aside.) (sinks upon a chair.)

M. Hé - las!
Ah me!

a piacere

W. Tu se - ras bien trai - té - e où je t'en-voi - e.
They will treat you most kind - ly, where I shall send you.

Nº 11. "Adieu, Mignon!"

Mélodie.

(1) The 1st verse *ad lib.* may be omitted.

Un poco animato
W.
pas!
pray!
Puisses-tu retrou-ver et fa-
May the Fates un-to home and to
poco animato
f
p
mil - le et pa-tri - e! Puisses - tu rencontrer en chemin le bon-heur!
kin - dred re-store you! May you meet on-ly joy while you go on your way!
p
Je te quit-te à re-gret et mon âme at-tendri - e Par-ta - ge ta dou-
I de-part with re - gret; for the tri-al before you My heart is sore to-
pp
dim.
Tempo I.
leur.
day!
A-dieu, Mignon, cou-ra - ge! ne pleu - re pas!
Fare-well, Mignon! Be joy - ous! Weep not, I pray!
pp
pp

pp

W. Les chagrins sont bien vite ou-bli-és à ton â-ge;
For in your ten-der years sor-rows ne'er long an-noy us;

cresc.

W. Dieu te con-so-le-ra, Dieu te con-so-le-ra! Mes voeux sui-
Heav'n will your woes al-lay, Heav'n will your woes al-lay! I wish you

f *poco cresc.*

poco rit. *p*

W. vront tes pas, mes voeux suivront tes pas! Ne pleu-re pas!
well al-way! I wish you well al-way! Weep not, I pray!

dim. *p* *segue* *poco più*

Ped. *

2nd Verse.

animato *p*

W. N'ac-cu-se pas mon coeur de-
Do not ac-cuse my heart of

W. froi-de in-dif-fé-ren-ce! Ne me re-proche pas de suivre un fol-a-
cold re-solve to sev-er, Re-proach me not of seek-ing wan-ton love in

W.
mour. En te di-sant a-dieu je
vain; While bid-ding you fare-well, my
pp
gar-de l'es-pé-ran-ce De te re-voir un jour. A-
hope is now and ev-er To see you once a-gain! Fare-
p
pp
Tempo I.
dieu, Mi-gnon, cou-ra-ge! Ne pleu-re pas!
well, Mi-gnon! Be joy-ous! Weep not, I pray!
pp
cresc.
Dieu te con-so-le-ra! Mes voeux sui-vront tes pas, mes
Heav'n will your woes al-lay, I wish you well al-way, I
cresc.
cresc.
mf
rit.
dim.
voeux sui-vront tes pas! A-dieu, ne pleu-re pas!
wish you well al-way! Fare-well! Weep not, I pray!
dim. col canto
p
pp

W.
sf
dim.
pp rall.
Recit. Mignon.
M.
Mer-ci de tes bon-tés; mais sans toi, Je veux ê-tre li-bre comme autrefois!
I thank you for it all; but if we part, I fain would be free to do as I will.
p
M.
La rai-son est cru-el-le, maî-tre! le cœur vaut
But if rea-son be cru-el, mas-ter! The heart's more
Wilhelm.
W.
É-cou-te la rai-son!
Let reason be your guide!
M.
mieux.
kind!
p
Ce que j'é-
Just what I
W.
Hors de cet-te mai-son que vas-tu de-ve-nir?
Tell me what you will be, when you go from this house?

Andantino con moto.
M.
tais: Mi-gnon!
was: Mi-gnon!
À mes ha-bits de Bo-hé - mien-ne Je re-viens, pour tou-
Then I shall wear my Gypsy garments once a-gain, and for
a tempo
Allegro.
jours.
life!
Wilhelm
(offering her a purse.)
W.
Ac-cepte au moins ce-ci!
At least accept of this!
De l'argent?
Money too?
non!
No!
p
(tenderly.)
ta main Seule-ment dans la
If on-ly your hand you will
Allegro.
f
p
(seizing Wilhelm's hand and carrying it to her lips.)
f
mien-ne, et je pars heu-reu-se!
give me, I shall leave you, hap-py!
mer-ci!
I thank you!
dim. e rit.
a tempo
Wilhelm.
Non! tu ne peux par-tir ain-si!
No! you can nev-er leave me thus!
Il le faut!..
But I must!
An-gois - se cru-el -
Oh heart - rending an -
riten.
p

Nº 11bis "Demain je serai loin."

Recitative.

(forcing a laugh.)
(bursting into tears.)
f
dim.
p
M.
pain. Ah! ah! ah! ah! ah! ah! ah! ah! ah! ah! ah!
try! Ah! ah! ah! ah! ah! ah! ah! ah! ah! ah! ah!
p>
f
dim.
Filina (appears in background with Frederick.)
Moderato.
M.
F.
Vous disiez vrai; Mignon de mes a-tours pa-
'Tis as you said: Mignon disport-ing in my
p
Recit.
(to Wilhelm, ironically.)
F.
ré - e!
dress-es!
El - le a bien - tôt quit - té vo - tre li-
The liv - er - y she wore, soon she dis-
Wilhelm.
W.
Phi - li - ne!
Fi - li - na!
F.
vré - e!
card - ed!
(with embarrassment.)
W.
Un ca-pri - ce d'en-fant qu'il faut lui par-don - ner.
The ca-price of a child, that you sure-ly for - give!

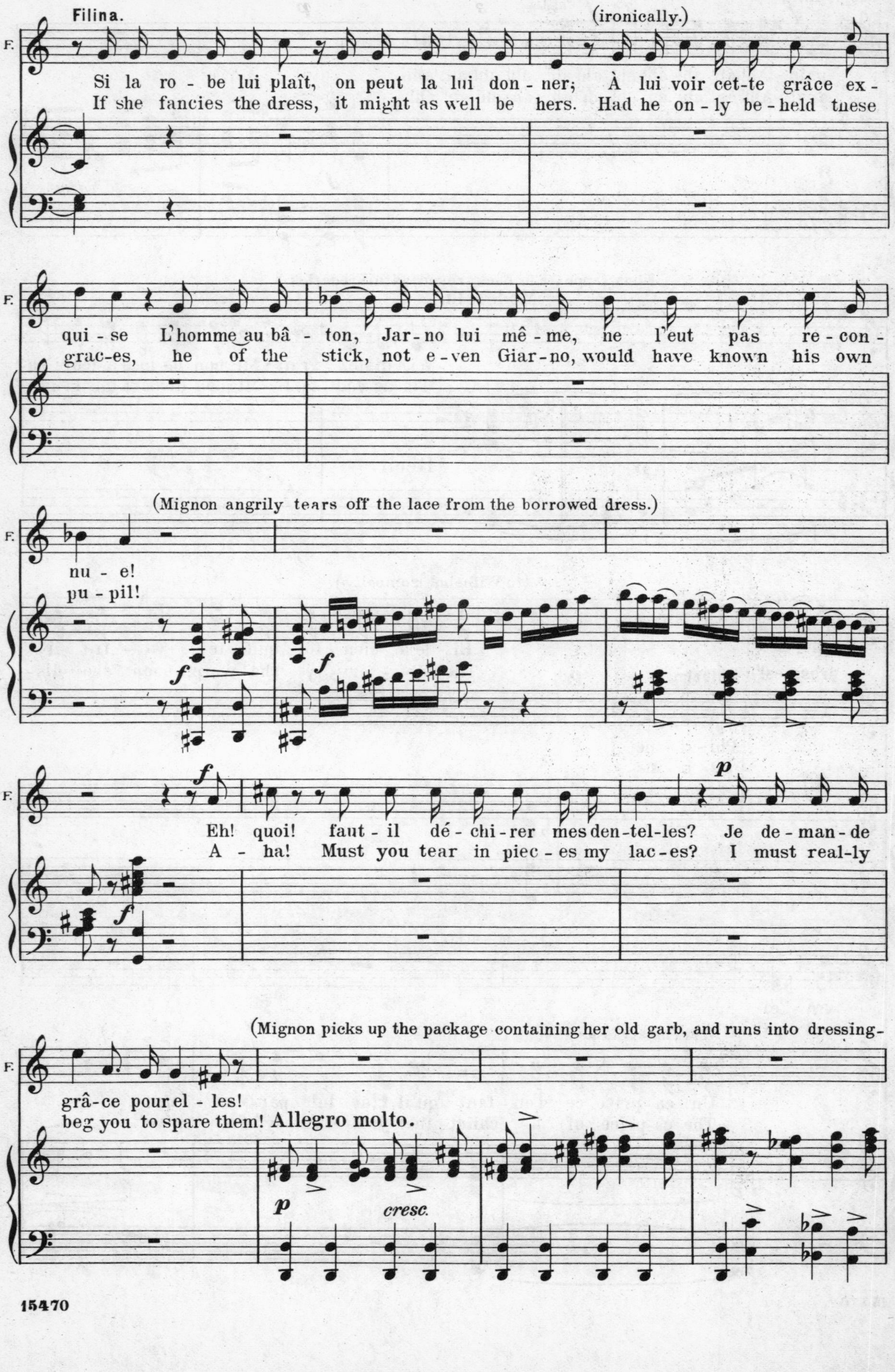

Filina.
(ironically.)
F.
Si la ro - be lui plaît, on peut la lui don - ner; À lui voir cet-te grâce ex -
If she fancies the dress, it might as well be hers. Had he on - ly be - held these
qui - se L'homme au bâ - ton, Jar - no lui mê - me, ne l'eut pas re - con -
grac - es, he of the stick, not e - ven Giar - no, would have known his own
(Mignon angrily tears off the lace from the borrowed dress.)
nu - e!
pu - pil!
f
Eh! quoi! faut - il dé - chi - rer mes den - tel - les? Je de - man - de
A - ha! Must you tear in piec - es my lac - es? I must real - ly
p
(Mignon picks up the package containing her old garb, and runs into dressing-
grâ - ce pour el - les!
beg you to spare them! Allegro molto.
cresc.

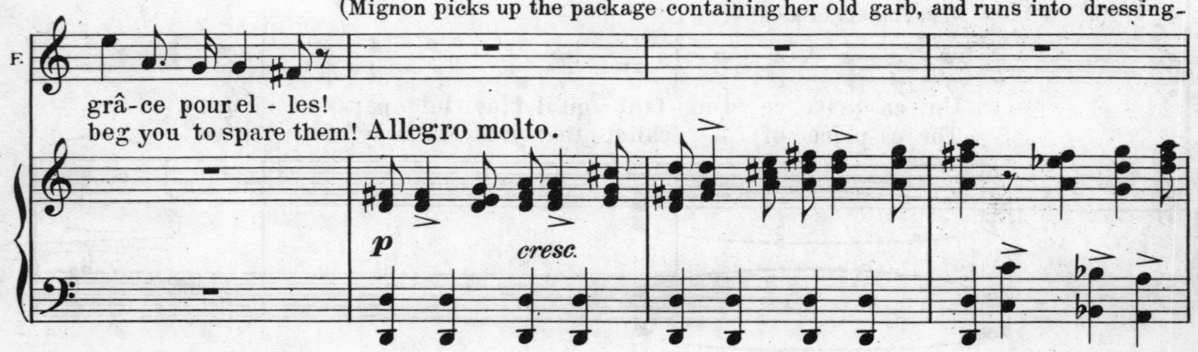

room, L.H.)

F. *f* (smiling.)

Quel courroux! Quel re-gard! On di-rait, sur ma foi, Que cet-te pauvre en-fant est ja-lou-se de moi!
What a rage! What a look! On my word, one would say That this poor child is jeal-ous of me, in a way!

W. Wilhelm (aside.)

Ja-lou-se!
She jealous!

Allegretto. (♩=84.)

(Enter Laertes hastily, attired as Prince Theseus.)

L. Laertes.

Eh bien! que fai-tes-vous? A-ler-te! on com-men-ce!
What are you all a-bout? Come on! We're be-gin-ning!

F. Filina.

Sui-vons La-ër-te.
We'll on, La-er-tes!

W. Wilhelm (aside.)

Ja-lou-se!
She jeal-ous?

F. Filina (to Wilhelm, smilingly.) *p*

A quoi rê-vez-vous donc?
What are you dreaming now?

Wilhelm.
Filina.
F.
W.
Je vous at-tends! Par-don! Of-frez-moi vo-tre bras,
I wait for you! Excuse me! Then pray give me your arm!
tr
tr
Wilhelm (aroused from his revery.)
Si vous m'ai-mez en-co-re! Qui? moi? Phi-li-
If you are still my lov-er! Who? I? Fi-li-
W.
f
ne, Je t'a-do-re!
na, I a-dore you!
3
cresc.
Frederick. (watching Filina and Wilhelm go out.)
Fr.
f
Morbleu! Qu'a-vec plai-sir
By heav'n! With what de-light
fp

(Mignon reappears in her costume
of Act I.)
Fr.
Je le mas-sa - cre - rais!
I'd rid the world of him!
fp
cresc.
Mignon.
ad lib.
Allegro moderato.
M.
Cet - te Phi - li - ne! je la hais!
Ah, that Fi - li - na! how I hate her!
ff
fp
Change on
open scene.

Second Tableau.

In the park adjoining the Baron's castle. R. H., at back, a conservatory brilliantly illuminated; L. H. a lake, with reeds, grasses, etc. Music and applause resound from behind the scenes: Mignon comes forward, and stops to listen.

Andante. (𝅗𝅥 = 56.)

Nº 12. "Elle est là! près de lui!"

Recitativo-Cantabile and Duet.

Agitato.
mf
dim.
p
Andante. (♩.=54)
Mignon.
M.
Elle est ai-me - e! il l'ai-me!
She is be-lov - ed! He loves her!
p
p
Eh bien! je le sa-vais! Ces tour-ments, je les é-prou-
Ah me! I knew it well! In my heart these torments did
sf
vais. Non! je ne l'a-vais pas en-ten-du de sa bou-che, Ce
dwell. No! I have nev-er known him to say in such fash-ion, This
p dim.
pp

cresc.
p
M.
mot qui dé-chi-re mon cœur! Es-pè-res-
word that is rend-ing my heart! Was it thy
cresc.
f
M.
tu que ton cha-grin_le tou-che? Pau-vre Mi-
hope, thy woe might win_com-pas-sion? Ah! poor Mi-
8
cresc.
largamente
M.
gnon! il l'ai-me! Ah!
gnon! He loves her!
8
Variant. (Soprano.)
f
Ah! son ri-re
Ah! her laugh-ter
M.
et son ri-re mo-queur Rend plus cruel-le en-cor,
And her smile is a dart, Ren-d'ring more cru-el yet,
8
f

Variant.
f
cresc.
rend plus cru - el - le cet - te pa -
ren - ders more cru - el the word he
M.
cresc.
plus cru - el - le cet - te pa - ro - le! Il
yet more cru - el the word he ut - ters! He
p
Variant.
ro - le! Hé - las! il l'ai -
ut - ters! A - las! he loves
M.
l'ai - me! Il l'ai -
loves her! He loves
dim.
M.
me! O Dieu! je de - viens
her! Ah, heav'n! my rea - son
M.
cresc.
fol - le! Dieu! je de - viens fol - le de
tot - ters! Heav'n! my - rea - son tot - ters From

(1) Should the voice execute this variant, the 1st clarinet *tacet* during this measure.

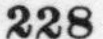

(2)

Vo-tre voix! Ah! j'en - tends
from be-low, Ah! I hear,

M.

seaux, Vo-tre voix, ô fil - les des
reeds, From be - low, how voic - es do

Vo-tre voix,
from be - low,

M.

eaux, J'en - tends vo - tre
call, I hear from be-

Ped. * Ped. *

1st Variant. (A)
voix, ô fil - les des
low, how voic - es do

2nd Variant. (A bis)
voix, ô fil - les des
low, how voic - es do

M.

voix, ô fil - les des eaux, J'en - tends, j'entends vo - tre
low, how voic - es do call! I hear, I hear how they

pp

Ped. *

Allegro moderato.

M.

cresc.

voix! Vous m'ap - pe - lez à vous, vous m'ap - pe - lez!
call! The daughters of the lake call me to come!

cresc.

(2) Should the voice execute this variant, the 1st clarinet *tacet* during these two measures.

Andantino.

M.

ff

(Harps)

M.

Ciel! qu'en-tends-je?
Heav'ns! What mu-sic!

M.

é - cou - tons!
I would hark!

Andantino con moto.

M.

Le mau-vais ange a
All e-vil thoughts are

p

sf

M. fui! Ah! je veux
fled! Ah, I would

sf

(enter Lothario.)

M. vi - - vre!
live!

cresc.

Variant Recit.

p
Est - ce toi, Lo - tha - rio?
Is it thou, Lo - tha - rio?

M.
L.
p
Est - ce toi, Lo - tha - rio?
Is it thou, Lo - tha - rio?

Lothario. (not recognizing her.)
p
Qui donc est
Who can be

f
p

Mignon.
M. *p*
C'est lui!
'Tis he!

Lo. là? Quelle est cet - te voix qui m'ap - pel - le?
there? What voice do I hear, that is call - ing?

(gazing at her tenderly.)
L.
Est-ce toi, Spe-ra-ta?...
Is it thou, Spe-ra-ta?
Ré-ponds, est-ce
Re-ply! is it
(gently repulsing her.)
a tempo
Mignon.
Lothario.
L.
M.
toi? Non! Mon cœur se trompe en-co-re, hé-
thou? No! My heart a-gain de-ceives me! Ah
p
p
L.
las! ce n'est pas el-le!
me! 'tis not Spe-ra-ta!
C'est l'en-
'Tis the
poco string.
L.
M.
fant qui vou-lait me sui-vre, C'est Mi-gnon!
child who was fain to join me: 'tis Mi-gnon!
Mignon.
p
Oui,
Yes,
p

Lotbario.
M. L.
oui, tu te souviens! oui, c'est bien là mon nom. Pauvre enfant! pauvre cré - a -
yes! you can re-call! yes, 'tis in-deed my name. My poor child! Thou un-hap-py
L.
tu - re! J'ai vou - lu te re - voir et j'ai sui - vi tes
crea - ture! To be - hold thee a - gain, long have I fol - low'd
a tempo
pas! Viens sur mon cœur! reste en mes bras! Et dis-moi quel cha -
thee! Come to my arms! Rest on my heart! Let me know all the
riten.
dim.
grin te brise et te tor-tu - re.
grief that bur-dens and torments thee!
mf
dim.

Duet.

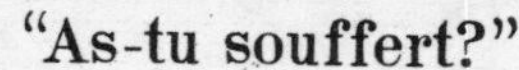

"As-tu souffert?"

Andante. (♪=72.)

Mignon. (leaning on Lothario's shoulder.)

p

As-tu souf-fert? as-tu pleu-ré? As-tu langui sans es-pé-rance?
Hast thou e'er wept? Dost thou know pain? Be-reft of hope didst e'er thou languish,

Piano. *pp*

cresc. *f* *p*

L'âme en deuil, le cœur dé-chi-ré? A-lors tu con-nais ma souf-france! Tu con-nais ma souf-fran-ce!
Dark thy soul, thy heart rent in twain? Ah, then thou knowest well my anguish! thou knowest well my an-guish!

poco animato *p* *dim.* *rit.* *p* *un poco riten.*

Lothario. *poco ritenuto* *p* *cresc.*

Comme toi triste et so-li-tai-re, Cour-bé sous d'in-fle-xi-bles lois,
Like thy-self, lone-ly and em-bit-ter'd, Bow'd down be-neath un-bend-ing skies,

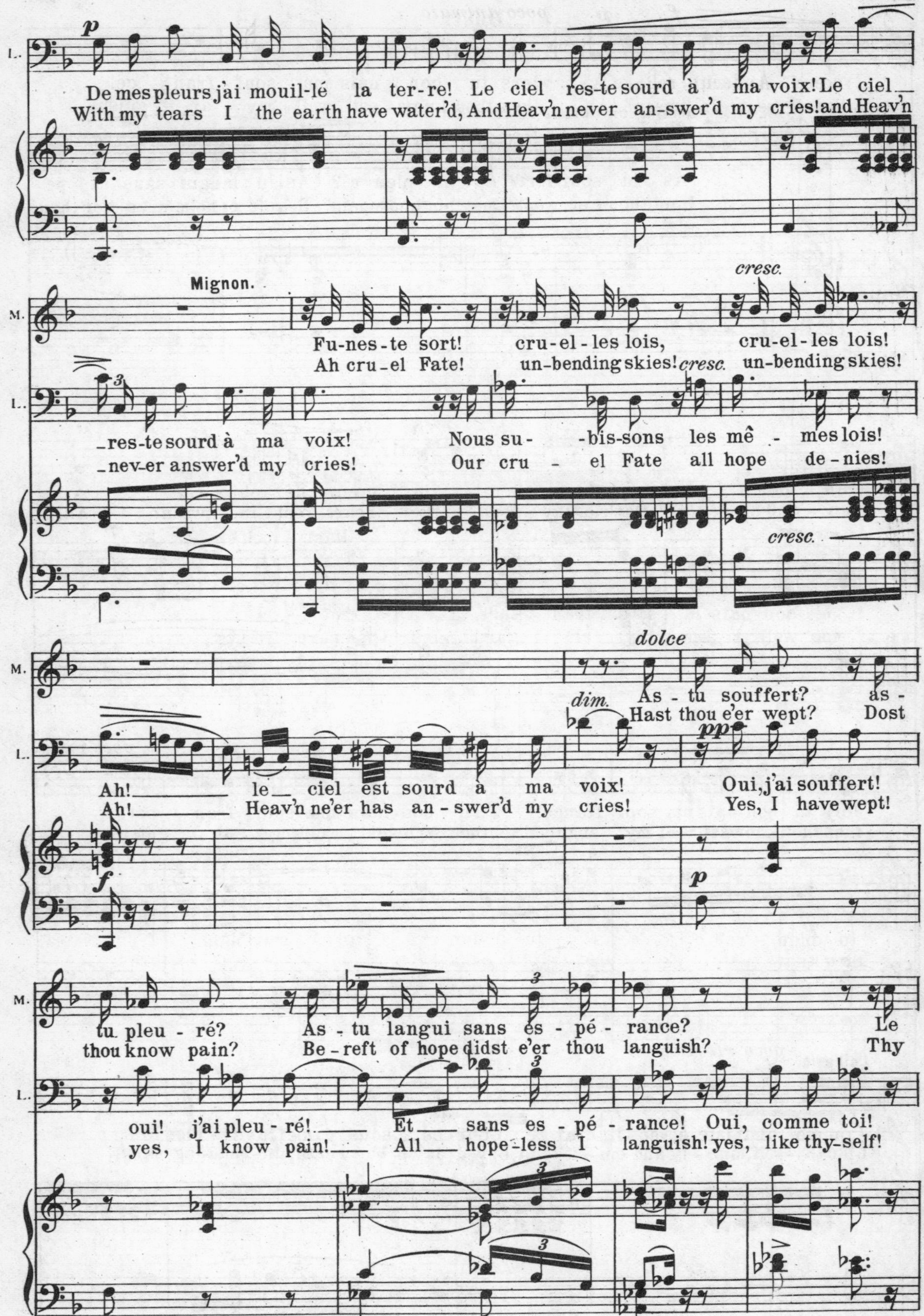
L.
p
De mes pleurs j'ai mouil-lé la ter-re! Le ciel res-te sourd à ma voix! Le ciel
With my tears I the earth have water'd, And Heav'n never an-swer'd my cries! and Heav'n
Mignon.
M.
cresc.
Fu-nes-te sort! cru-el-les lois, cru-el-les lois!
Ah cru-el Fate! un-bending skies! un-bending skies!
_res-te sourd à ma voix! Nous su-bis-sons les mê-mes lois!
_nev-er answer'd my cries! Our cru-el Fate all hope de-nies!
cresc.
dolce
As-tu souffert? as-
dim.
Hast thou e'er wept? Dost
pp
Ah! le ciel est sourd à ma voix! Oui, j'ai souffert!
Ah! Heav'n ne'er has an-swer'd my cries! Yes, I have wept!
f
p
tu pleu-ré? As-tu langui sans es-pé-rance? Le
thou know pain? Be-reft of hope didst e'er thou languish? Thy
oui! j'ai pleu-ré! Et sans es-pé-rance! Oui, comme toi!
yes, I know pain! All hope-less I languish! yes, like thy-self!
3

f
p
poco animato
M.
cœur dé-chi-ré? A - lors tu con-nais ma souf-fran - ce!
heart rent in twain? Ah, then thou know-est well my an - guish!
L.
En - fant!
My child!
p
As - tu souffert? As-
Hast thou e'er wept? Dost
dim.
je con-nais la souf-fran - ce! Oui, j'ai pleu - ré! Oui, j'ai souf-
too well I know thy an - guish! Yes, I have wept? yes, I know
dim.
tu pleu - ré? As - tu lan-gui, lan - gui sans es-pé-ran-
thou know pain? Be - reft of hope didst ev - er thou_ lan-
dim.
fert! hé-las, oui, j'ai lan-gui_ sans es-pé-ran-
pain! Ah me! be - reft of hope_ ev - er I lan-
dim.

M.
cresc.
ce, Et l'âme en deuil, le cœur dé-chi-ré? A-
guish? All dark thy soul, thy heart rent in twain? Ah,
L.
cresc.
ce, Oui, com-me toi, le cœur dé-chi-ré! En-fant,
guish! Yes, like thy-self, my heart rent in twain! My child!
cresc.
f
p
lors, a-lors tu con-nais ma souf-fran-ce! As-tu souffert? as-
then, ah then thou know-est well my an-guish! Hast thou e'er wept? Dost
f
p
je connais, je con-nais la souffran-ce! Oui, j'ai souffert, oui,
well I know, well do I know thy an-guish! Yes, I have wept, Yes,
pp
Moderato.
tu pleu-ré?
thou know pain?
j'ai pleu-ré!
I know pain!
(Applause is heard behind the scenes.)
Moderato. (𝅗𝅥 = 76.)
cresc.

Variant.
É-cou-te! c'est son nom que la fou-le ré-
But list-en! 'Tis her name that the throng is re-
Mignon.
M.
É-cou-te! c'est son nom que la fou-le ré-
But list-en! 'Tis her name that the throng is re-
Recit.
pè-te! C'est el-le qu'on ac-cla-me et c'est el-le qu'on fê-te.
peat-ing! 'Tis she whom they ac-claim, it is she all are greet-ing!
pè-te! C'est el-le qu'on ac-cla-me et c'est el-le qu'on fê-te.
peat-ing! 'Tis she whom they ac-claim, it is she all are greet-ing!
Ah! que la main de Dieu ne peut-el-le sur
Ah! and the hand of God, where-fore doth it not
eux faire é-cla-ter la fou-dre, Et frapper ce pa-
launch His light-ning's aw-ful flash-es, Rend the pal-ace in

(The door of the conservatory opens, and a throng of guests, actors, etc., issues.)

No. 12bis "La Philine est vraiment divine."

Chorus.

The Prince, the Baron and Baroness, Filina and the comedians, Frederick, Ladies and Gentlemen. Servants bearing torches. The theatrical performance within is supposed to have just ended; Filina and the other comedians are still wearing their stage-costumes.

(1) This introduction may be shortened by cutting the next 8 measures, to the sign ⊕.

(1) The next 24 measures may be omitted, by skipping to the sign ф on page 242.

Quel tri - om - phe et quel suc - cès!
To hail it is our du - ty!
Cé - lé - brons ses at - traits!
Let her charm all con - fess!
Quel tri - om - phe et quel suc - cès!
To hail it is our du - ty!
p
mf
cresc.
Ah, quel tri - omphe et quel suc - cès!
Ah, how tri - umphant her suc - cess!
Ah! quel suc -
Hail her suc -
Chan - tons ses at - traits!
All her charm con - fess!
Ah, quel tri - omphe et quel suc - cès!
Ah, how tri - umphant her suc - cess!
p
cresc.
cès!
cess!
f
Ah! bra - va!
Ah, bra - va!
f
La Phi - line est vraiment di -
Ah, Fi - li - na, di - vine thy
f
f
ff

(1) If the singer is unable to execute the Polonaise, skip from here to the Finale, page 255.

No. 12ter "Oui, pour ce soir je suis reine."

Recitative, Polonaise and Finale.

dim.
F.
d'or,
wand,
p
Ped.
p
(pointing at her wreaths)
f
Et voi - ci mes tro -
and be - hold all my
ff
phé - es!
tro - phies!
f
p
Frederick.
Fr.
p
Dé - jà vingt a - mants En - tou - rent la
Man - y own the spell By Fi - li - na
Chorus.
Actors, Actresses and some Gentlefolk.
tr

Fr.
bel - le!
wield-ed! SOPRANO II.
bel - le! Et tout est pour el - le, Fleurs et compliments!
wield-ed! All to her is yield-ed, Flow'rs and hearts as well!
bel - le!
wield-ed!
Et cet-te cru-el - le Rit de nos tourments!
Cru-el - ly she smil-eth On our torment fell!
tr
ff
Polonaise.
"Je suis Titania."
Moderato tempo di Polacca. (♩ = 96.)
Filina.
F.
f
Je suis Ti-ta-ni-a la
I am Ti-ta-ni-a, the
mf
blon - de, Je suis Ti-ta-ni-a, fil - le de l'air, En ri-
fai - ry, I am Ti-ta-nia, daughter gay of air! Roaming

F.
cresc.
dim.
ant__ je parcours le mon-de, Plus vi-ve que_ l'oiseau, plus prompte
ev-'rywhere, and ev-er mer-ry, Than swal-low swift-er_ I,_ than lightning
que__ l'é-clair!
bold- -er far!
Je_
I_
suis Ti-ta-ni-a la blon-de, Ah!
am Ti-ta-ni-a, the fai-ry, Ah!
Ah!
Ah!
Je parcours le mon-de,
Roam-ing ev-er mer-ry,
ah!
ah!
ah!
ah!
cresc.
ah!
ah!

F.
ah!
ah!
ah!
ah!
cresc.
ah! Plus vi - ve que l'oi -
ah! Than swallow swift - er
f
p
seau, plus prompte que l'é-clair!
I, than lightning bolder far!
ah!
Ah!
Je suis Ti-ta-ni-a la blon - de, Je
I am Ti-tan-i-a, the fai - ry, I
ff
pp
suis Ti-tani-a, fil - le de l'air! En ri-ant je parcours le mon - de, Plus vi - ve
am Titania, daughter gay of air! Roaming ev-'ry-where, and ev-er mer - ry, Than swallow
dim.
que l'oi-seau, plus prompte que l'éclair!
swift-er I, than light-ning bold - er far!
Je
I

(1) Should it be desired to shorten this piece, the best cut would be to skip from here (1) to the sign ⊕ on page 251.

F.
La trou-pe fol-le des lu-tins Suit
The wan-ton fai-ries on my way stray,
Mon char qui vole et dans la nuit Fuit,
My car they fol-low night or day, aye!
senza rigore
— Au ra-yon de Phœ-bé qui luit! Par-
— By ten-der Phœ-be's wand'ring ray! 'Mid
pp
dim.
mi — les fleurs que l'au-ro- - re Fait é-
wak - - 'ning flow - - ers, the morn - - ing Fair a-
pp
clo - - re,
dorn - - ing,
dolce
Par les bois et par les prés Di-a-prés,
O-ver hill and o-ver dale On we sail!
cresc.
Sur — les flots cou-verts d'é-cu - - me, Dans la —
O'er — the o - - cean-bil-low foam - - ing In — the —

dolciss.
F.
bru - me, On me voit d'un pied lé - ger Vol-ti-ger!
gloam - ing, You may see_ me dance a-way Ev-er gay!
D'un pied lé - ger par les bois, par les prés, Et dans la
Light - - ly_ I sail O-ver hill, o-ver dale, And, ev - er
brume On me voit vol - ti - ger, On me voit vol - ti - ger!
gay, I am danc-ing a-way! I am danc-ing a-way!
mf
Ah! ah! Voi -
Ah! ah! a -
cresc.
f
f

F.
là! Ti-ta-ni-a! Ah!
way! Danc-ing a-way! Ah!
sempre cresc.
cresc.
ff
ff
En ri-ant— je par-cours le
Roam-ing ev-'ry-where and ev-er
p
poco rit.
a tempo
f
mon- de, Plus vi-ve que l'oi-seau, plus prompte qui l'é-
mer- ry Than swal-low swift-er I, than light-ning bold-er
colla voce

animato un poco
F.
clair!
far!
Ah!
Ah!
p
accel.
cresc.
tr
f
ff
Je suis Ti-ta-ni-a, fil-le de
I am Ti-ta-ni-a, daugh-ter of

(1) The next 5 measures may be omitted, in which case the singer goes on from the sign ⌖.

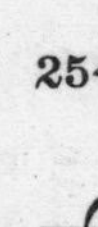

F.

Frederick.

Fr.

Gloi - - re! gloi - re à Ti - ta - ni -
Hail we, hail we, hail we Ti -

SOPRANO.

Gloi - - re! gloi - re à Ti - ta - ni -
Hail we, hail we, hail we Ti -

TENOR.

Gloi - - re! gloi - re à Ti - ta - ni -
Hail we, hail we, hail we Ti -

BASS.

p cresc. *ff*

Fr.

a! ta - - - - nia!

a! ta - - - - nia!

a! ta - - - - nia!

(1) Chord connecting the Polonaise with the ballet *ad libitum.*

Finale.

(Enter Wilhelm, Mignon, and Lothario.)

Allegro moderato. (𝅗𝅥 = 76)

Wilhelm (with a preoccupied air).
Filina.
W.
F.
Pardonnez-moi! je cherche en vain Mi - gnon. Eh! quoi!
Pardon, I pray! I seek Mignon in vain. Indeed!
Fr.
ten - dre!
fond - ly!
(they retire, conversing.)
Lothario (to Mignon).
sotto voce
F.
Lo.
Cel - le que vous cherchez, monsieur, ce n'est pas moi. Sois con -
She you are looking for, Monsieur, it is not I! Now be
(𝅗𝅥 = 69)
Lo.
ten - te, Mi - gnon. ré - jou - is - toi, pauvre
glad, O Mi - gnon! You may re - joice, poor
Lo.
â - me! J'ai vou - lu te ven - ger, et ces murs sont en
crea - ture! I have sought to a - venge you; the pal - ace is

Mignon.
M.
Ciel!
Heav'ns!
que dis - tu?
what say you?
Lo.
flam - - me!
burn - - ing!
J'ai fait ce que tu vou -
I've done as you de -
(She looks around anxiously; Wilhelm hurries toward her.)
Dieu!
Heav'ns!
cresc.
lais! Ces murs vont s'écrou - ler sous des torrents de feu!
sir'd! 'Tis I, all o-ver-whelming, set-ting all on fire!
Wilhelm.
Filina (to Mignon).
W.
F.
Ah! Mignon! te voi - là! je te cherchais! Ho - là! ho - là! ma
Ah, Mignon! you are here! 'Twas you I sought! Hal - loh! halloh! my
Mignon (to Filina).
Filina.
bel - le! Que voulez-vous? Pour nous prouver ton
fair one! What is your will? To prove your zeal to
marc.

F.
3
zè - le, Va vi - te me chercher là-bas, sur le thé - âtre, Un bouquet dont mon-
serve us, a-way, seek me with-in the hall, up-on the stage, a bouquet that mon-
F.
sieur, tantôt, m'a fait hom-ma - ge Et que j'ai laissé choir, je crois, de mon cor-
sieur presented me so kind - ly, and that I have let fall, I think, some-where with-
m.d.
(exit hastily into conservatory.)
Mignon.
F.
M.
sa - ge. J'o-bé - is, maî - tre, j'o-bé - is!
in there. I o - bey! Mas - ter, I o - bey!
Wilhelm.
W.
A quoi bon?..
What's the use?
cresc.
sf
sf
sf
sf
sf
sf

Laertes (rushing in).
Dieu!
Ah!
Phi-li - ne! mes a-
Fi-li - na! on-ly
mis, mes a-mis,
see, on-ly see!
le théâtre est en feu! Regar-
All the stage is on fire! On-ly
dez!
look!
Frederick.
Que dit-il?
All on fire?
le feu! le
On fire! on
SOPRANO.
Ah!
Ah!
le feu! le
on fire! on
TENOR.
Que dit-il?
All on fire?
le feu! le
on fire! on
BASS.
Chorus.

Filina.
F.
Je meurs! mon sang se gla - ce!
My heart freez-es in hor - ror!
Wilhelm.
W.
Ah!
Ah!
Fr.
feu! le
fire! On
feu! le
fire! On
feu! le
fire! On
F.
Ah! mon sang se gla - ce!
Ah! freez-es in hor - ror!
Fr.
feu!
fire!
Laertes. (stopping Wilhelm.)
La.
Wil-helm!
Wil- helm!
feu! Le
fire! On
feu! Le
fire! On

F. J'i-gno-rais le dan-ger, Le ciel m'en est té-moin! Wil-helm!
I knew naught of the dan-ger, may Heav'ns bear wit-ness now! Wil-helm!

Wilhelm.
W. Ah! mal-heu-reu-se en-fant!
Ah! That un-hap-py child!

feu! fire!

feu! fire!

Wilhelm.
W. Ne me re-te-nez pas!
Ah, do not hold me back! (rushes out)

Laertes.
La. Ar-rê-tez!
Do not go!

SOPRANO. Pour To

TENOR. Pour To

BASS.

Moderato.
a - pai - ser la flam - me, Pour con - ju - rer le mal, tout se -
quell the con - fla - gra - tion, Its aw - ful pow'r to en - chain, Hu - man
a - pai - ser la flam - me, Pour con - ju - rer le mal, tout se -
quell the con - fla - gra - tion, Its aw - ful pow'r to en - chain, Hu - man
Moderato. (♩= 116)
ff
cours se - rait vain, tout se - cours se - rait vain, L'ef -
aid is in vain, hu - man aid is in vain, Ap -
cours se - rait vain, tout se - cours se - rait vain, L'ef -
aid is in vain, hu - man aid is in vain, Ap -

froi gla - ce no - tre â - me! L'ef - froi gla - ce no - tre â - me! Que sert -
pal - ling de - vas - ta - tion! Ap - pal - ling de - vas - ta - tion! What no
froi gla - ce no - tre â - me! L'ef - froi gla - ce no - tre â - me! Que sert -
pal - ling de - vas - ta - tion! Ap - pal - ling de - vas - ta - tion! What no
Fr.
Frederick.
Vo - yez!
Be - hold
La.
Laertes.
Vo - yez!
Be - hold
il de ten - ter un ef - fort sur - hu - main!
man e'er can do, where - fore seek it a - main!
il de ten - ter un ef - fort sur - hu - main! Vo - yez!
man e'er can do, where - fore seek it a - main! Be - hold

Filina.
F.
Fr.
La.
f
Ah! vo - yez! vo - yez la
Ah! be - hold the con - fla -
vo - yez la flam - - - me!
the con - fla - gra - - - tion!
vo - yez la flam - - - me!
the con - fla - gra - - - tion!
Ah! vo - yez! vo - yez la
Ah! be - hold the con - fla -
vo - yez la flam - - - me!
the con - fla - gra - - - tion!
ff
flam - me! Dieu! le thé - âtre est en
gra - tion! Heav'ns! The stage is all on
L'effroi glace notre â - - me!
Ap - pal - - ling de - vas - ta - - tion!
L'effroi glace notre â - - me!
Ap - pal - - ling de - vas - ta - - tion!
flam - me! Dieu! le thé - âtre est en
gra - tion! Heav'ns! The stage is all on
L'effroi glace notre â - - me!
Ap - pal - - ling de - vas - ta - - tion!
ff

F.
feu! Vo-yez! le thé-âtre est en feu!
fire! Be-hold! all the stage is on fire!
Fr.
Vo-yez! le thé-âtre est en feu!
Be-hold! all the stage is on fire!
La.
Vo-yez! le thé-âtre est en feu!
Be-hold! all the stage is on fire!
feu! Vo-yez! le thé-âtre est en feu!
fire! Be-hold! all the stage is on fire!
Vo-yez! le thé-âtre est en feu!
Be-hold! all the stage is on fire!
Lothario. (aside)
Lo.
Fu-gi-tif et trem-
Still from door un-to
dim.

Lo.
blant
door
je vais
all way
ff
Le feu!
The fire!
ff
Le feu!
The fire!
ff
ff
Lo.
de por te en por te.
worn I am go ing,
ff
Le feu!
The fire!
ff
Le feu!
The fire!
ff
ff

Lo.
3
3
Où le ha - sard me gui - - -
Wher - ev - er Fate may guide
ff
Le
The
ff
Le
The
ff
6
Lo.
de; où l'o - ra - - - - - ge m'em -
me, or the storm - - - wind be
feu!
fire!
feu!
fire!
ff
Lo.
cresc.
por - - te! Des mi - sé - ra - - bles
blow - - ing! For them who mourn, the
p

Filina.
ff
F.
Pour a - paiser la flam - me, Pour con - jurer le
To quell the con - fla-gra - tion, Its aw - ful pow'r t'en-
Frederick.
ff
Fr.
Pour a - paiser la flam - me, Pour con - jurer le
To quell the con - fla-gra - tion, Its aw - ful pow'r t'en-
Laertes.
ff
La.
Pour a - paiser la flam - me, Pour con - jurer le
To quell the con - fla-gra - tion, Its aw - ful pow'r t'en-
Lo.
Dieu prend soin! El-le vit! el-le
Lord will care! She's a-live, still a -
ff
Pour a - paiser la flam - me, Pour con - ju-rer le
To quell the con - fla-gra - tion, Its aw - ful pow'r t'en-
ff
Pour a - paiser la flam - me, Pour con - ju-rer le
To quell the con - fla-gra - tion, Its aw - ful pow'r t'en-
ff
f
ff

F.
mal, tout se - cours se - rait vain, tout se -
chain, Hu - man aid is in vain, hu - man
Fr.
mal, tout se - cours se - rait vain, tout se -
chain, Hu - man aid is in vain, hu - man
La.
mal, tout se - cours se - rait vain, tout se -
chain, Hu - man aid is in vain, hu - man
Lo.
vit!
live!
mal, tout se - cours se - rait vain, tout se -
chain, Hu - man aid is in vain, hu - man
mal, tout se - cours se - rait vain, tout se -
chain, Hu - man aid is in vain, hu - man

F.
cours se-rait vain, L'ef-froi gla-ce notre
aid is in vain! Ap-pal-ling de-vas-
Fr.
cours se-rait vain, L'ef-froi gla-ce notre
aid is in vain! Ap-pal-ling de-vas-
La.
cours se-rait vain, L'ef-froi gla-ce notre
aid is in vain! Ap-pal-ling de-vas-
Lo.
Et je cherche sa tra-ce!
Ev-er seek I her trac-es!
cours se-rait vain, L'ef-froi gla-ce notre
aid is in vain, Ap-pal-ling de-vas-
cours se-rait vain, L'ef-froi gla-ce notre
aid is in vain, Ap-pal-ling de-vas-
ff

F.
â - me! L'ef - froi gla - ce notre â - me! Que sert-
ta - tion! Ap - pal - ling de - vas - ta - tion! What no
Fr.
â - me! L'ef - froi gla - ce notre â - me!
ta - tion! Ap - pal - ling de - vas - ta - tion!
La.
â - me! L'ef - froi gla - ce notre â - me!
ta - tion! Ap - pal - ling de - vas - ta - tion!
â - me! L'ef - froi gla - ce notre â - me! Que sert-
ta - tion! Ap - pal - ling de - vas - ta - tion! What no
â - me! L'ef - froi gla - ce notre â - me!
ta - tion! Ap - pal - ling de - vas - ta - tion!
F.
il de ten - ter un ef - fort sur-hu-
man e'er can do, where-fore seek it a-
Fr.
Que sert-il de ten-ter un ef-fort
What no man e'er can do, where-fore seek
La.
Que sert-il de ten-ter un ef-fort
What no man e'er can do, where-fore seek
il de ten - ter un ef - fort sur-hu-
man e'er can do, where-fore seek it a-
Que sert-il de ten-ter un ef-fort
What no man e'er can do, where-fore seek

F.
main! Tout se - cours se-rait
main! Hu-man aid is in
Fr.
sur-hu-main! Tout se - cours se-rait
it a-main! Hu-man aid is in
La.
sur-hu-main! Tout se-cours
it a-main! Hu-man aid
main! Tout se - cours se-rait
main! Hu-man aid is in
sur-hu-main! Tout se-cours
it a-main! Hu-man aid
F.
vain!
vain!
Fr.
vain, tout se-cours se-rait vain!
vain, our aid would be in vain!
La.
se-rait vain, oui, se-rait vain!
is in vain, is all in vain!
vain, tout se-cours se-rait vain!
vain, our aid would all in vain!
se-rait vain, oui, se-rait vain!
is in vain, is all in vain!
(the walls fall down.)
fff

(all rush in terror to front.)
ff
F.
Ciel!
Heav'ns!
ff
Fr.
Ciel!
Heav'ns!
ff
La.
Ciel!
Heav'ns!
ff
Ciel!
Heav'ns!
ff
Ciel!
Heav'ns!
ff
8
dim.
f

Wilhelm (panting; he bears Mignon in his arms).
W.
De la mort Dieu l'a pre-ser-vé-e!
From the fire God him-self pre-serv'd her!
Au de-vant du dan-ger el-le semblait cou-rir!
In the midst of the dan-ger she es-cap'd all harm!
Con-tre son dé-ses-poir j'ai pu la se-cou-rir!
'Spite of her own des-pair, I held her in my arm!
La flam-me l'en-tou-rait dé-jà, je l'ai sau-
The flames al-read-y rose a-round I sav'd her

F.
Ah! sau - vés, sau - vés!
Ah! They're saved! they're saved!
W.
vée!
life!
Fr.
Ah! sau - vés, sau - vés!
Ah! They're saved! they're saved!
La.
Ah! sau - vés, sau - vés!
Ah! They're saved! they're saved!
Ah! sau - vés, sau - vés!
Ah! They're saved! they're saved!
Ah! sau - vés, sau - vés!
Ah! They're saved! they're saved!

(Wilhelm lays Mignon on a bank; she still holds the withered bouquet.)

End of Act II.

Act III.

Nº 13. "Au souffle léger du vent."

Introduction, Chorus and Berceuse.

A gallery adorned with statues. R.H., a window with wide view of the country: at back. a closed door; a door at either side. As the curtain rises, the stage is unoccupied: a harp-prelude is heard from behind the scenes.

Allegro moderato.
Chorus. (behind the scenes).
SOPRANO I.
dim.
riten.
Ah! ah!
SOPRANO II.
Ah! ah!
TENOR I.
Ah! ah!
TENOR II.
Ah! la la la la la la la la
BASS I.
Ah! la la la la la la la la
BASS II.
Ah! la
Allegro moderato. (♩. = 72)
Au souf-fle lé-ger du vent
Now on we sail be-fore the wind,
Au souf-fle lé-ger du vent
Now on we sail be-fore the wind,
La la la la la la la la la la la la la la la la

p
— Ouvrons gaî - ment nos voi - - les; À la clar-té des é -
— So en-chant - ing - ly sigh - - ing; The stars in glo-ry are
p
—— Ou-vrons nos voi - - - les; À la clar-té des é -
—— enchant-ing-ly sigh - - ing; The stars in glo-ry are
p
— la la la la la la la la la la la la la la la
p
— la la la la la la la la la la la la la la la
p
— la la la la la la la la la la la la la la la
p
— la la la la la la la la la la la la la la la
f p
toi - les, Ah! — Sui - vons le flot mou - vant. — Dans la
vy - ing, Ah, — the waves fol - low be - hind. — The oar
f p f
toi - les, Sui - vons le flot mou - vant. — Dans la
vy - ing, The waves fol - low be - hind. — The oar
f p
la la la la — la la la la la la la la la la la
f p
la la la la — la la la la la la la la la la la
f p
la la la la — la la la la la la la la la la la
f p
la la la la — la la la la la la la la la la la

ff
nuit la rame é-tin-celle Et laisse a-près elle Un sil-lon de feu, Sur
gleaming white in the night, Is cleav-ing a fur-row, a fi-e-ry wake, O'er
nuit la rame é-tin-celle Et laisse a-près elle Un sil-lon de feu, Ah!
gleaming white in the night, Is cleav-ing a fur-row, a fi-e-ry wake, O'er
f
La rame é-tin-cel-le sur le lac bleu, Ah!
Gleam-ing on the lake, Leaves a fie-ry wake! Ah!
dim.
le lac bleu.
the blue lake.
pp
Au souf-fle lé-
Now on we sail be-
ah!
La la la
p
ah

(1) If desired, the next 16 measures, which are a repetition, may be cut, in which case continue from the sign ⊕ on page 283.

dim.
ff
celle Et laisse a-près elle Un sil-lon-de feu, Sur le lac bleu.
night, Is cleav-ing a fur-row, a fi-e-ry wake, O'er the blue lake!
celle Et laisse a-près elle Un sil-lon-de feu, Ah!
night, Is cleav-ing a fur-row, a fi-e-ry wake, Ah!
é-tin-cel-le Sur le lac bleu. Ah!
on the lake, Leaves a fie-ry wake! Ah!
é-tin-cel-le Sur le lac bleu. Ah!
on the lake, Leaves a fie-ry wake! Ah!
é-tin-cel-le Sur le lac bleu. Ah!
on the lake, Leaves a fie-ry wake! Ah!
é-tin-cel-le Sur le lac bleu. Ah!
on the lake, Leaves a fie-ry wake! Ah!
pp
f
p
Au souf-fle lé-ger du vent
Now on we sail be-fore the wind,
Au souf-fle lé-ger du vent
Now on we sail be-fore the wind,
ah! La la la la la la
La la la la la la
ah! La la la la la la
ah! La la la la la la

p

— Ou-vrons gaî-ment nos voi - - les! À la clar-té des é -
— So en-chant-ing-ly sigh - - ing; The stars in glo-ry are

p

— Ou-vrons nos voi - - les! À la clar-té des é -
— en-chant-ing-ly sigh - - ing; The stars in glo-ry are

p

— la la la la la la la la la la la

p

— la la la la la la la la la la la

p

— la la la la la la la la la la la

p

— la la la la la la la la la la la

f p B mf

toi-les Ah! Sui-vons le flot mou-vant! Ah! la
vy-ing, Ah, the waves fol-low be-hind. Ah! la

f p mf

toi-les Sui - vons le flot mou-vant! Ah! ah!
vy-ing, The waves fol-low be-hind. Ah! ah

f p mf

la la la la la la la! Ah! ah!

f p mf

la la la la la la la! Ah! ah!

f p mf

la la la la la la la! Ah! ah!

f p mf

la la la la la la la! Ah! ah!

la la *p* ah! ah! ah!

ah! ah! *p* ah! la la

ah! ah! *p* ah! la la

ah! ah! *p* ah! ah! ah!

ah! ah! *p* ah! ah! ah!

ah! ah! *p* ah! ah! ah!

ah! ah! ah! ah! ah! *sf* ah! *p* la la la

la ah! ah! *sf* ah! *p* la la la

la ah! ah! *sf* ah! *p* la la la

ah! ah! *sf* ah! *p* la la la

ah! ah! *sf* ah! *p* la la la

la la *sf* ah! *p* la la la

pp
smorz.
ff
la! Ah! ah! ah! ah! ah! ah!
La la la
la! Ah! ah! ah!
La la la
la! Ah! ah! ah!
La la la
la! Ah! ah! ah!
La la la
la! Ah! ah! ah!
La la la
la! Ah!
La la la
Andantino con moto.
la!
la!
la!
la!
la!
la!
Andantino con moto. (♪ = 116.)
p
(Lothario enters from door R. H.)
dim.

Berceuse.

Lothario.
p
L.
De son cœur j'ai cal-mé la fiè-vre! Un sou-ri-re doux et joy-
From her heart the fe-ver de-part-ed! E'er my voice her woe al-
pp
eux À ma voix entr'ouvrant sa lè-vre, Le som-meil a fer-mé ses
lays; By a smile her lips were part-ed, Slum-ber ten-der-ly clos'd her
poco cresc.
yeux. Pauvre en-fant! Dieu te pro-tége et te dé-fend!
eyes. Ah, poor child! May God be ev-er-more thine aid!
rit.
Dors en paix! dors, pauvre en-fant, pauvre en-fant!
Ah, poorchild! Slumber in peace, ten-der maid!
colla voce
sf
dim.

dolce
L.
Sur son front é-ten-dant son ai-le, Et pour
O'er thy brow his pin-ions ex-tend-ing, May an
pp
el-le quit-tant les cieux, Un bon an-ge veille auprès
an-gel leave the skies, Thee from sor-row ev-er de-
pp
d'el-le! Le som-meil fer-me ses
fend-ing! Now may slum-ber seal thine
poco cresc.
yeux. Pau-vre en-fant! Dieu te pro-
eyes! Ah, poor child! May God be
tége et te dé-fend!
ev-er-more thine aid!
pp
Dors en paix!
Ah, poor child!
pp

presto un poco
rit.
L.
dors, pauvre en - fant! pauvre en - fant! Dieu te pro-tége et te- dé-
Slum-ber in peace, ten-der maid! May God be ev-er-more thine
colla
voce pp
pp
L.
fend! Pauvre en - fant!
aid! thine aid!
Allegretto moderato.
SOPRANO I.
Chorus.
Ah!
Ah!
SOPRANO II.
Allegretto moderato.
pp
La rame é-tin-celle Et laisse a-près elle Un sil-lon de
The gleam-ing oar white Doth leave in the night A wide, fi-e-ry
TENOR I.
La rame é-tin-cel-le sur le lac
Gleam-ing on the lake, Leaves a fie-ry
TENOR II.
La rame é-tin-cel-le sur le lac
Gleam-ing on the lake, Leaves a fie-ry
BASS I.
La rame é-tin-cel-le sur le lac
Gleam-ing on the lake, Leaves a fie-ry
BASS II.
La rame é-tin-cel-le sur le lac
Gleam-ing on the lake, Leaves a fie-ry

f dim. p

feu, Sur- le lac bleu. Au- souf-fle lé-
wake, o'er the blue lake! Now on we sail be-

feu. Ah! Au- souf-fle lé-
wake, Ah! Now on we sail be-

bleu. Ah! La la la
wake, Ah! La la la

bleu. Ah! La la la
wake, Ah! La la la

bleu. Ah! La la la
wake, Ah! La la la

bleu. Ah! La la la
wake, Ah! La la la

sf p

ger du vent Ouvrons gaî-ment nos voi - les; À la clar-té des é-
fore the wind, So en-chant-ing-ly sigh - ing; The stars in glo-ry are

ger du vent Ou-vrons nos voi - les; À la clar-té des é-
fore the wind, enchant-ing-ly sigh - ing; The stars in glo-ry are

la la la la la la la la la la la la la la

la la la la la la la la la la la la la la.

la la la la la la la la la la la la la la

la la la la la la la la la la la la la la

sf p

toi - les, Ah! Sui-vons le flot mou-vant! Ah! ah!
vy - ing, Ah, the waves fol-low be-hind! Ah! ah!

toi - les Sui - vons le flot mou-vant! Ah!
vy - ing, The waves fol-low be-hind! Ah!

la la la la la la la! Ah! ah! ah!

la la la la la la la! Ah! ah! ah!

la la la la la la la! Ah! ah! ah!

la la la la la la la! Ah!

pp smorz. rit.

la la la la! Ah! ah! ah! ah! ah! ah! ah!

la la la la! Ah! ah! ah!

la la la la! Ah! ah! ah!

la la la la! Ah! ah! ah!

la la la la! Ah! ah! ah!

la la la la! ah! ah!

Allegro moderato.
Recit.
(Setting a lamp on a table. and turning toward the window).
Antonio.
Vous ver-rez de cet-te fe - nê-tre s'il-lu-mi-
You will see, on near-ing this win-dow, how all the
Piano.
A.
ner les vil-las d'a-len-tour; De la fê-te du lac c'est de-main le grand
vil-las are lighted a-round; for to-mor-row the fête on the lake will be
A.
jour; Ce pa-lais seul, de-puis qu'il a per-du son maî-tre, ne s'il-lu-mi-ne
held. This pa-lace here a-lone, since it has lost its mas-ter, is lighted up no
Wilhelm.
A.
W.
plus! Oui, l'on m'a ra-con-té qu'une en-fant dans les flots ja-dis per-dit la
more! Yes, the tale I have heard: That a child in the lake long years a-go did
Antonio.
W.
A.
vi - e. La pau-vre mère, hé-las! dans la mort l'a sui-
per - ish. The moth-er too, a-las! soon in death fol-low'd

A.
vi - e; fou de dou - leur, son père a pour ja - mais quit - té l'I - ta -
af - ter; craz'd by their loss, the fa - ther left his na - tive country for
A.
li - e; et bien - tôt le toit de ses an - cê - tres de - vra pas - ser à d'au - tres
ev - er; ver - y short - ly his an - ces - tral man - sion will be possess'd by oth - er
Wilhelm.
W.
De - main je ré - pon -
To - morrow I shall de -
A.
maî - tres. S'il est en - core à vo - tre gré, Vous pou - vez l'a - che - ter.
own - ers. If you still find it to your mind, it is yours for a price.
Allegro moderato.
(laying his hand on Lothario's shoulder)
p
W.
drai.
cide. (exit Antonio at a sign from Wilhelm)
Eh
What
bien?
now?
mf a tempo
dim.
p
Lothario.
p
L.
Chut!... Un sou - rire a pas - sé sur la lè - vre; L'en - fant
Hush! O'er her fea - tures a smile e'en was pass - ing; she's a -

Wilhelm (joyfully).
Ah! que le ciel en soit bé-
Ah! Let us praise kind Heav'n there-
dort et n'a plus la fiè-vre.
sleep, she has no more fe--ver.
ni! C'est l'air na-tal qui la rappelle à la vi-e! Oui, de-
for! Her na-tive air now un-to life has re-stored her! Yes, for
main j'a-che-te-rai pour el-le le pa-lais des Cy-pri-
her to-mor-row I shall pur-chase the a-bode of the Ci-pri-
a-ni!
a-ni!
Lothario (rises, trembling)
Qu'as-tu?
What then?
Cy-pri-a-ni?
Ci-pri-a-ni?
Allegro.
Andante. (♪= 112)
(Lothario goes to the great door at back, and tries to open it)

Wilhelm.
Lothario.
W.
L.
p
Cet-te chambre est fer - mé-e de-puis quinze ans! Quin- -ze ans?
Yon-der room has been clos'd for these fift - teen years! Fif - teen years?
(Lothario goes to door L.H.)
L.
p
Ah! là!
Ah! there!
(turning toward Wilhelm)
pp
L.
Chut!...
hush!
(exit slowly)
Moderato. Recit.
Wilhelm. (alone)
W.
smorz.
É-tran - ge re -
How strange was his
W.
gard! Ah! mieux que ma rai - son le cœur de ce vieil-lard Con-so - le cet en -
look! Ah, bet - ter than my will, the heart of this old man has com-fort-ed this

W.
fant par ses soins ra-ni-mé-e! J'ai de-vi-né trop tard le-se-cret de Mi-
child, whom his cares have re-viv-ed! Too late, a-las, I've guess'd what Mi-gnon has con-
(Softly opening door R.H.)
(tenderly)
gnon; Hé-las! el-le som-
ceal'd! Ah me! while yon-der
(If the Romance be sung in D♭, skip to the sign ⊕.)
meil-le, et pro-non-ce mon nom.
sleep-ing, she pro-nounc-es my name!
(Go on with the Romance in C)
⊕ (For the Romance in D♭.)
rit.
Hé-las! el-le som-meil-le, et pro-non-ce mon nom.
Ah me! while yon-der sleep-ing, she pro-nounces my name!
(Go on with the Romance in D♭.)

Nº 14. "Elle ne croyait pas."

Romance. (1)

(1) This Romance may be transposed into D♭, as it was sung by M. Achard at the Opéra-Comique.

pp
son rê - ve de bon - heur. Pour ren - dre à la fleur é - pui -
her tran - quil vi - sion blest! To glad - den the flow-er des -
poco più ritenuto (♪= 58.)
sé - e Sa fraîcheur, son é - clat ver - meil, Ô prin -
pair - ing, To re - vive all her ro - sy glow, Balm - y
pp
temps, don - ne - lui ta gout - te de ro - sé - e!
Spring, on her heart let fall thy dew re - stor - ing!
f
riten.
Ô mon cœur, don - ne - lui, don - ne - lui ton ra - yon de so -
Oh my heart, on her way, on her way all thy sun-shine be -
colla voce

W.
leil!
stow!
f
Ped. * Ped. * Ped. *
W.
C'est en vain
'Tis all in
mf
p
pp
W.
que j'attends un a - veu de sa bou - che, Je veux con - naître en vain
vain I wait for an a - vow - al ten - der, 'Tis all in vain I seek
p
poco cresc.
W.
ses se - crè - tes douleurs, Mon re - gard l'in - ti - mi - de et ma voix
to guess her se - cret woe; She shrinks be - fore my gaze, my words her
pp

W.
pp
l'ef- fa - rou - che, Un mot trou - ble son âme et fait cou - ler ses pleurs!
fear en - gen - der, Tho' I be ne'er so kind, her tears do ev - er flow!
poco cresc.
Pour ren - dre à la fleur é - pui - sé - e Sa fraî -
To glad - den the flow - er des - pair - ing, To re -
un poco più ritenuto
cheur, son é - clat ver - meil, Ô prin -
vive all her ro - sy glow, Balm - y
pp
Ped.
temps, don - ne - lui ta gout - te de ro - sé - e!
Spring, on her heart let fall thy dew re - stor - ing!
Ped.

W.
Ô mon cœur, don-ne-lui, don-ne-lui ton ra-yon de so-
Oh my heart, on her way, on her way all thy sunshine be-
colla voce
rit.
leil!
stow!
dim.
rall.
Allegro.
(taking the letter, and
Que me veux-tu?
Whatwould you have?
Mer-
'Tis
Antonio.
A.
Si-gnor! Cet-te let-tre...
Si-gnor! 'Tis a let-ter
Allegro.
dismissing him.)
(exit Antonio)
(reading)
ci!
well!
"Phi-li-ne vous sui-vait,
"Fi-li-na fol-low'd you;
a tempo

(hastening towards Mignon's chamber)

W. fu-yez, elle est i-ci!" Un a-vis de La-er-te!.. Ah! Mi-gnon!

a-way, for she is here!" 'Tis a hint from La-er-tes! Ah! Mi-gnon!

riten.

(stopping) *p* la voi-ci! She ap-pears!

dim.

(He draws back: Mignon enters without noticing him)

Andante sostenuto. (♪= 96)

pp

Mignon. *p* Où suis-je? Je res-pire un air plus doux, L'a-zur est plus pro-fond!..

Where am I? 'Tis a soft-er air I breathe, and blu-er are the skies!

sempre dolce

Dans le flot pur de ce lac transpa-

And in the lake so transpa-rent I

dim. *pp*

M.
rent se re-fléte un bois som-bre!... U-ne
see a dark for - est re-flect-ed! and a
voile y glis - se dans lom-bre!... Quel - le fraî-
sail in shad - ow is glid - ing! Fresh 'tis, and
dim.
cheur!... Et ce pa-lais dont les jar-dins des-cendent vers la grè - ve,
cool! And this pal-ace, with its gar-dens sloping to the lake - side:
rit.
Il me semble avoir vu tout ce-la dans un rê-ve... Lothari-o! Wilhelm!
'Tis as if I had seen it be-fore in a vision! Wil-helm! Lothario!
Wilhelm. (hastening to her)
W.
Mi-
Mi-
pp
p

Nº 15. "Je suis heureuse! l'air m'enivre."

Duet.

Wilhelm.
W.
Pau - vre en-fant! plus de crain - tes vai - nes!
Ah! poor child! fear thou vainly no lon - ger!
sf
cresc.
Un air plus pur va te ra - ni-mer, Un sang nou-
A kind - lier air laves thee from a-bove, And flows thy
veau gon - fle tes vei - nes, Mi-gnon doit vi - vre pour ai-
life - stream ev - er stron - ger: Mi-gnon shall live to know my
p
mer. Ah! tu dois vi - vre, tu dois vi - vre pour ai-
love! Ah! thou shalt live, thou shalt live to know my
cresc.
f
Mignon.
M.
f
dim.
p
pp
mer, tu dois vi - vre pour ai - mer! Oui,
love! thou shalt live to know my love! Yes,
p
pp

M.
je te crois, je veux te croi-re! Par-le-moi, parle en-
I be-lieve, I'd fain be lieve you! Say it o'er yet a-
Wilhelm.
M.
W.
p
cor, tou-jours! Chasse à ja-mais de ta — mé-moi-re
gain, a-gain! Ban-ish for ev-er what may grieve you,
p
a tempo
M.
p
Je suis heu-reu-se! L'air m'en-
My heart no lon-ger pines for-
riten.
W.
Le sou-ve-nir — des mau-vais jours.
Ev'ry re-mem-brance fraught with pain!
colla voce
a tempo
M.
i-vre, mon — cœur a ces-sé de souf-frir.
sak-en, Balm-y airs — dis-pel all un-rest!

Wilhelm.
W.
mf
cresc.
f
Oui, crois au bon-heur qui t'en-i - vre, Ton
No more shall your heart pine for-sak - en, All
tr
cresc.
f
p
Mignon.
M.
mf
Je re-nais, je me sens re-
Here a-new to life I a-
W.
dim.
mf
cœur a ces-sé de souf-frir! Pour ai-mer Mi-gnon de-vait
woe shall de-part from your breast! Un-to love Mi-gnon doth a-
8
un poco riten.
M.
p
f
vi - vre, Mi-gnon ne craint plus de mou-rir! Je re-nais, je me sens re-
wak - en, Of death now no fear fills my breast! Here a-new un-to life I
W.
p
f
vi - vre, Mi-gnon ne pou-vait pas mou-rir! Pour ai-mer Mi-gnon de-vait
wak - en, By love be her life ev - er blest! Un-to love Mi-gnon doth a-
p
un poco riten.
mf
f
un poco riten.
M.
p
vi-vre, Mi-gnon ne craint plus de mou-rir! Ah! Mi - gnon
waken, Of death now no fear fills my breast! Ah! of death
W.
p
vi-vre, Mi-gnon ne pou-vait pas mou-rir! Ah! Mi - gnon
waken, By love be her life ev - er blest! Ah! by love
p
un poco riten.

M.
W.
rit.
dim.
ne craint plus de mou-rir!
now no fear fills my breast!
rit.
ne pou-vait pas mou-rir!
be her life ev-er blest!
p
cresc.
f
pp
rall.
Andante. (♪ = 104)
Wilhelm.
pp
Ah! que ton âme en-fin
Ah, may thy soul at last
dans mon â-me s'é-pan-che!
in-to mine all be streaming!
poco cresc.
Chè-re Mi-gnon! chè-re Mi-
Dear-est Mi-gnon! dear-est Mi-

W.
gnon! lè - ve vers moi, lè - ve vers moi - tes
gnon! raise un - to me, raise un - to me thine
smorz.
W.
yeux. Sous ce ray - on di - vin, et dans ta ro - be blan - che, Tu m'ap - pa -
eyes! Un - der this ray di - vine, And in thy gar - ment gleam - ing, Thou dost ap -
W.
dim.
mf
rais com - me un an - ge des cieux! Ah!
pear like an an - gel from the skies! Ah!
mf
dim.
W.
p
lè - ve vers moi tes yeux! Tu m'ap - pa - rais comme un an - ge des
raise un - to me thine eyes! Thou dost ap - pear like an an - gel from the
pp
Mignon. (smiling sadly)
M.
p
Non, c'est tou - jours Mi - gnon.
No, it is still Mi - gnon!
W.
pp
cieux! Mi - gnon n'est plus la
skies! Mi - gnon, and yet an -
un poco riten.
pp
un poco riten.

(aside, in ecstasy) *pp*

M. O Dieu! dois-je le croi-re?
O Heav'n! Dare I be-lieve it?

W. même.
other.

poco cresc.
Mi-gnon a tout mon cœur, et c'est
Mi-gnon has all my heart! Her a-

pp

Variant
Dois-je le croire,— est-ce bien moi
Dare I be-lieve— that I am she

M. Dois-je le croire, est-ce bien moi qu'il ai-me?
Dare I be-lieve— that I am she he lov-eth?

W. el - - - - - le que j'ai-me!
lone ———— it a-dor-eth!

pp

Allegro.
Mignon. (slowly) *a tempo*

M. Toi m'ai-mer! que dis-tu?
You love me? Can it be?

f *p*

M. sou-viens-toi du pas-sé...
Put re-mem-ber the past:

Ton cœur est à Phi-
Your heart is all Fi-

sf *p* *sf*

M.
li - ne...
li - nas!
Est-il vrai? ô
Is it true? oh
a piacere
Wilhelm.
W.
Phi-line est loin de nous, et je ne l'ai-mais pas.
I love Fi-li-na not, and she is far a-way!
f
p
ff
joie i-nef-fable et di-vi-ne!
joy, oh di-vin-est of rap-tures!
risoluto
Je puis en-
Now I at
pp
fin te di-re... mais par-lons bas, par-lons bas, bien
last may tell you_ But let us speak ver-y low, speak
dim.
Moderato.
Filina. (behind the scenes)
M.
F.
bas! Je_ suis Ti-ta-ni-a la blon-de, Je_ suis Ti-ta-ni-a, fil-
low! I_ am Ti-ta-ni-a, the fai-ry, I_ am Ti-ta-nia, daugh-ter
mf

F.
le — de l'air! En ri - ant — je parcours le mon - de, Plus vi - ve
gay — of air! Fare o'er land or o-cean ev - er mer - ry, Than swal - low
Wilhelm (aside.)
W.
M.
Phi-li - ne!
Fi-li - na!
Mignon.
p (aside.)
En-cor el - le!
'Tis Fi - li - na!
F.
M.
que l'oi-seau, plus promp-te - que — l'é-clair!
swift - er I, — than light-ning bold - - er far!
Mignon
(running to the window.)
En-co-re cet-te
This woman yet a -
mf
p
F.
Je — suis Ti-ta-ni-a la blon - de! Ah! —
I — am Ti-ta-ni-a, the fai - ry! Ah! —
M.
fem - me!
gain! —
Ô mon secret,
Secret of love,
mf
p
F.
f
p

F.
M.
Reste au fond de mon â - me.
in my heart lie for ev - er!
string.
presto
tr
Allegretto. (♩.=80)
Mignon.
Ah!
Ah!
(jealously.)
Je re - connais sa voix, Je l'en-tends, je la
Her voice it is I hear, That I know, that I
vois. C'est elle en - cor, c'est el - le Qui te cherche et t'ap -
fear! 'Tis she a - gain doth call you, Seek-ing you to en -

M.
pel - le! Ne m'in-ter-ro-ge pas! Je dois me taire, hé -
thrall you! Ah! nev-er ask me now! Well, that I still for -
las! Je ne veux plus par - ler, Je ne par - le-rai
bore! I have no more to say, I will say no-thing
8
f
p
f
pas, Hé-las! Je ne veux plus par -
more! Ah me! I have no more to
f
ff
ler, Je ne par-le-rai pas, Je ne par-le-rai
say, I will say no-thing more, I will say no-thing
p
Wilhelm (lovingly.)
un poco rit.
M.
W.
pas! Non, non, non, non, non, non! je ne par-le-rai pas! Je n'en -
more! No, no, no, no, no, no! I will say no-thing more! 'Tis thy -
un poco rit.
f
ff
p

(1) If desired, the next 10 measures may be cut, skipping to the sign ⊕ on page 315.

F.
la la la la la la la la la la la la la la la la la la la la la la la la la la la la
M.
Mignon (aside.)
p
En-co - re!
Still sing - ing!
F.
cresc.
la la la la la la la la la la la la la la la la la la la la la! ah! ah!
M.
cresc.
Ah! Ah! c'est
Ah! Ah! Fi-
F.
M.
el - le!
li - na!
Wilhelm.
f
Je re-connais sa
Her voice it is I
W.
Mi-gnon, je n'entends que ta voix,
Mi-gnon, 'tis thy voice that I hear!
cresc.
animato
f
M.
voix, Je l'entends, je la vois, C'est elle encor, c'est el-le Qui te cher-che et t'ap-
hear, That I know, that I fear! 'Tis she again doth call you, Seeking you to en-
W.
C'est toi seu - le
'Tis thee on - ly
p
sf p

M.
pel - le; Ne m'in - ter - ro - ge pas! Je dois me taire, hé -
thrall you! Ah! nev - er ask me now! Well, that I still for -
W.
que je vois, toi seu - le que j'entends.
whom I hear, thee on - ly whom I hear!
f
p
p
M.
las! Je ne veux pas par - ler, Je ne par - le - rai
bore! I have no more to say, I will say nothing
W.
Tu dou - tes en - cor; Ah! tu ne m'ai - mes
You are still in doubt? Ah! you love me no
f
p
M.
f
pas! Hé - las! Je ne veux plus par -
more! Ah me! I have no more to
W.
f
pas! Ah! Hé - las, hé -
more! Ah! A - las, a -
f
cresc.
ff
M.
ler, Je ne par - le - rai pas, Je ne par - le - rai
say, I will say no - thing more, I will say no - thing
W.
las! tu ne m'aimes pas! non, tu ne m'ai - mes pas!
las! you love me no more! no, you love me no more!
p
cresc.

M.
pas. Ah! Ah! Ah! Ah! je ne veux plus par-
more! Ah! ah! ah! ah! I will say no-thing
W.
Ah! cru-el-le! tu ne m'ai-mes pas! Tu dou-tes en-
Ah! how cru-el! You love me no more! You are still in
ler, je ne par-le-rai pas. Ah!
more, I will say no-thing more! Ah!
cor, Oui, tu dou-tes en-cor. Hé-las!
doubt, yes, you are still in doubt! A-las!
Je ne par-le-rai pas, je ne par-le-rai
I will say nothing more, I will say nothing
Mignon ne m'ai-me pas! non! non! tu ne m'ai-mes
Mignon loves me no more, no, no, you love me no
(sinks on a seat.)
pas! Non! Non!
more! No! no!
pas! Hé-las!
more! Ah me!

dim.
p
Recit. Wilhelm.
W.
f
p
Ah! malheureuse en-fant... Ses mains sont gla-
Ah! the un-hap-py child! Her hands are as
Moderato sostenuto.
p
W.
cé-es...Cet-te voix maudi-te, ô mor-tel ef-froi, Réveille en son cœur les douleurs pas-
frozen! That accurs-ed voice, with a mortal dread, awakes in her heart all the woes de-
p
W.
rit.
sé-es! Mi-gnon, toi que j'ai-me, ah! re-viens à
part-ed! Mi-gnon, my be-lov-ed! ah! re-vive a-
p

(Mignon comes to her senses.)
(tenderly.)
W.
toi!.. Elle ou-vre les yeux!.. C'est moi qui t'ap-
gain! She o-pens her eyes! 'Tis I who have
rit.
W.
M.
Mignon.
p
pel - le! Je n'en-tends plus
call'd you! I can hear no
pp
M.
W.
Wilhelm.
mf
rien! n'est-ce pas un rê - ve? Non, ce n'estqu'un rê - ve! un rê - ve men -
more! Was it not a dream? Yes, 'twas but a vi-sion, a fe - ver-ish
W.
teur Où la fièvre en-co-re é - ga - re ton cœur.
dream that a-rose a-gain to trou-ble your heart.
pp

Mignon.
La fiè-vre, dis-tu? non!.. ce-lui qui m'ai-me c'est Lo-
A vi-sion, you say? No! The one who loves me is Lo-
tha-ri-o! Pourquoi n'est-il pas près de moi?
tha-ri-o! Why is he not near to me now?
(turning toward door at back.)
é-cou-te!
But list-en!
pp a tempo
Oui, j'entends son pas!
Yes! I hear his step!
Nul ne peut ve-nir de
No one can come in from
là!
there!
(The door at back suddenly flies open, and Lothario enters, richly attired, and carrying a small box.)
Mignon.
C'est lui-mê-me!
'Tis Lo-tha-rio!

No 16. "Mignon! Wilhelm! Salut à vous!"

Trio.

Mignon (astonished.)
W.
M.
di - re? Sous ces ri - ches ha - bits, est - ce lui que je
say - ing? In at - tire so su - perb, is it he whom I
p
pp
Lothario.
M.
L.
vois? Tout i - ci m'ap - par -
see? All is mine that you
(to Mignon.)
L.
tient; re - gar - de! ad - mi - re!...
see: Be - hold it! ad - mire it!
L.
En ce pa - lais, j'é - tais maître au - tre - fois!
Once in this pal - ace, the mas - ter was I!
Wilhelm (aside to Mignon).
W.
p
De sa fo - lie, hé - las! a - yons pi -
His fool - ish dreams, a - las! our pit - y
pp

Mignon.
W. M.
tié! Je ne re-connais plus son regard ni sa
crave! I nei-ther re-cog-nize his appear-ance nor his
dim.
Lothario.
M. L.
voix. Ou-bli-ons nos temps de mi-
voice! Let us now for-get all our
L.
sè-re, ou-bli-ons nos temps de mi-
sor-row, let us now for-get all our
dim.
L.
sè-re! Je t'ap-por-te un don pré-ci-eux, Il a-
sor-row! Thee I bring a gift passing rare; 'Twill al-
L.
dou-ci-ra, je l'es-pè-re, L'en-nui de ton cœur sou-ci-
lay, I hope, for ev-er All pain in thy heart full of

Allargate un poco.
Mignon (aside).
M.
p
cresc.
Quel est___ cet___ é-tran - ge mys - tè - re Que___ tra-hit___ l'é-clat,_ l'é-
What se - cret___ un-told,___ over-pow'ring, Doth___ the glance, the glance of his
Wilhelm (aside).
W.
p
cresc:
Quel est___ cet___ é-trange mys-tè - re Que___ trahit l'é-clat,_ l'é-
What se - cret___ un-told, o-ver pow'r - ing, Doth___ the glance, the glance of his
L.
cresc.
eux. Ou - blions nos___ temps, nos___ temps de___ mi-
care! Let us now for - get, for - get all___ our
Allargate un poco.
M.
f
p
f
riten. e dim.
clat de___ ses___ yeux? Quel est ce mys-tè - re Que tra-hit___ l'é-
eye now be - tray? What se-cret o'er-pow'ring Doth the glance of his
W.
f
f
riten. e dim.
clat___ de ses yeux? Quel est ce mys-tè - re Que tra-hit___ l'é-
eye___ now be-tray? What se-cret o'er-pow'ring Doth the glance of his
L.
f
p
sè - - re!
sor - - row!
f
p
f
colla parte

M. clat de ses yeux?
eye now be-tray?

W. clat de_ ses yeux, de ses yeux?
eye now be-tray, now be-tray?

L. de_ ton cœur sou - ci - eux.
'Twill al - lay all thy pain!

Andante sostenuto. (♩ = 52.)

Lothario (to Mignon).

L. Cet - te cas-sette est là
This lit - tle box has lain

De - puis ___ de bien longs mois; En -
for man - - y wear - y months. Child,

L. fant, tu peux l'ouvrir.
you may ope it now!

Mignon.
M. Que contient - el - le?
What is with - in it?

Lothario.
Vois! __
Look!

(Mignon opens the box.)
Mignon.
M.
Une é-char-pe d'en-fant!
'Tis a scarf for a child!
Lothario.
L.
D'or et d'argent bro-dé-e! Oui, je l'a-
Broi-der'd in gold and sil-ver! Yes, and with
M.
Quelle est cet-te re-lique, et qui donc la por-
What rel-ic may this be, and by whom was it
L.
vais pi-eu-sement gar-dé-e!
ten-der care have I pre-serv'd it!
M.
pp
ta! Par-le! Spe-ra-ta!
worn? Tell me! Spe-ra-ta!
L.
p
Spe-ra-ta!
Spe-ra-ta!

M.
Dé - jà ce nom a frap-pé mon o - reil - le...
That ver - y name in my ear has re - sound - ed—
Un sou - ve - nir loin - tain À ce doux nom dans mon â - me s'é -
A mem - o - ry long past at this sweet name in my soul re - a -
dim.
Lotario
(aside, sorrowfully).
M.
L.
p
veil - le! Est - ce l'é - cho loin - tain d'un pas - sé qui n'est plus?— Spe -
wak - ens! Is it an ech - o lone from a past dead and gone? Spe -
Mignon.
sf
dim.
Des pleurs, des pleurs mouil - lent ses yeux.
His eyes, his eyes are — fill'd with tears.
Wilhelm.
W.
Des pleurs, des pleurs mouil - lent ses yeux.
His eyes, his eyes are — fill'd with tears.
ra - ta!
ra - ta!
sf
p
pp

Lothario (to Mignon.)
Ne vois-tu pas aus-si un bra-ce-let de co-rail?
Do you not see, be-sides, a lit-tle brace-let of cor-al?
Mignon.
p
Le voici! Trop pe-tit pour mon bras!
Here it is! 'Tis too small for my arm!
mf
Trop grand, trop grand pour
Too large, too large for
sf
pp
p
el-le, El-le ne vou-lait pas at-ten-dre au len-de-
her! She could not bear to wait un-til the com-ing
poco cresc.
main Pour por-ter un bi-jou qui la ren-dait plus bel-le.
day, to put on such a chain that ren-der'd her more love-ly;
Mais le bi-jou tou-jours lui glis-sait de la
but ev-'ry time the chain slipp'd a-way o'er her

Mignon (aside, greatly moved.)

M. *p* Lui glis-sait de la main...
Slipp'd a-way o'er her hand_

L. W. main.
hand.

Wilhelm. *f* Qu'as-tu? tu
What is't? You

sf *p*

W. L. trembles et tu pleu-res! *p* Mi-gnon!
trem-ble, you are weep-ing! Mi-gnon!

Lothario. Regarde en-
Now look a-

pp

Mignon.

M. Un li-vre d'heu-res!
It is a prayer-book!

L. co - re!
gain, child!

Hé-las! je crois toujours la
Ah me! I think I see her

dim.

L. voir, lettre à let-tre, é-pe-ler sa pri-è-re du soir.
still, spell-ing let-ter by let-ter her ev-'ning prayer!

sf

Prayer.
"Ô Vierge Marie."
Andantino. (♪ = 116.)
Mignon (opening the book, and reading).
M.
p
Ô Vier - ge Ma - ri - e, Le Sei - gneur est a - vec
O Vir - gin all - ho - ly, Ev - er near our Sav - iour
pp
vous; A - bais - sez vos re - gards si doux Sur l'en -
blest, May thine eye now ten - der - ly rest On a
(letting the book fall, and finishing from memory, with uplifted eyes and folded hands.)
fant qui pri - e!
child so low - ly!
Lothario.
L.
pp
El - le pri - ait ain - si!
'Twas thus she used to pray!
pp
(hesitating.)
(recalling it.)
Vous qui ber - cez sur vos ge - noux Le di - vin sau -
Thou who dost hold up - on thy knee Him who rul - eth
pp
veur de la ter - re, Con - ser - vez l'en - fant a sa
all cre - a - tion, Him who died for our sal -
p

M.
mè - re! O ma - do - ne, pri - ez pour nous! pri - ez pour
va - tion, Vir - gin Ma - ry, ah, pray for me, ah pray for
pp
pp
Allegro. (𝅗𝅥 = 88)
M.
L.
Lothario (in great agitation,
nous!
me!
Est - ce Dieu qui l'ins -
Is it God who in -
pp
mf
holding out his hands to Mignon.)
L.
pi - re?..
spires her?
Elle a - chè - ve sans
With - out read - ing, she
mf
Mignon (gazing around her with increasing excitement.)
L.
M.
li - re!
ends it!
Lo - tha - ri - o!
Oh Lo - tha - rio!
M.
Wil - helm!
Oh, Wilhelm!
Suis - je donc en dé -
Am I los - ing my

M.
li - - re?..
sens - - es?
Je de-vi - ne!..
I di-vine it!
sf
je vois!..
I see,
sempre cresc.
Je sens!..
I feel!
je ne puis di - re!..
I can-not say it!
(to Wilhelm.)
Ou donc m'as-tu con-dui-te, et quel est ce pa-ys?
Ah, whither have you brought me? What coun-try is this?
I-ta-
'Tis
Wilhelm.
W.
f
L'I-ta-li-
'Tis I - ta-
fp
cresc.

M.
li - e! Ô ray - ons de cé - les - te lu - miè - re!
I - ta - ly! Ah! what ra - diance of sun - light ce - les - tial!
W.
e!
ly!
mf
(After a violent effort to recall dim memories, she rushes out of door at back with a wild cry, and almost instantly reappears, pale and trembling.)
f
Ô souve - nirs!
All I re - call!
cresc.
f
Recit.
f
Là! là! l'i - ma - ge de ma mè - re! Et sa chambre est dé -
There! there! the portrait of my mother! And her chamber is
p
p
a tempo
ser - te! Mon pè - re!
emp - ty! My fa - ther!
ff
Loth.
ff
L.
W.
L.
Wilhelm.
Lothario.
Ah! ma fil - le! Ah! C'est mon en -
Ah! My daugh - ter! Ah! It is my
8
a tempo
ff

M.
Oui! je vous re-con-nais!
Yes! I re-member you!
L.
W.
Wilhelm.
fant! C'est el - le! Se peut-il!
child! Spe-ra - ta! Can it be?
8
dim.
p
cresc.
ff
M.
Ô Dieu, je te bé-nis! Oui, je re-trou-ve mon
O Lord, I praise thy name! I find my fa - ther a -
ff
W.
El - le re-trouve en-fin, El-le re-trou-ve son
Ah! she has found at last, now she has found at last her
ff
L.
Ô Dieu, je te bé-nis! C'est el - le!
O Lord, I praise thy name! Spe-ra - ta!
8
ff
M.
père et mon pa - ys, mon
gain, my na - tive land! my
W.
père et son pa - ys, son
fa - ther, her na - tive land! her
L.
ô Dieu! je te bé - nis! C'est mon en -
O Lord, I praise thy name! She is my
8
ff

M.
père! mon pa - ys! Ô mon Dieu, je te bé -
own, my na - tive land! O my God, I praise thy
W.
père! son pa - ys! Ô mon Dieu, je te bé -
own, her na - tive land! O my God, I praise thy
L.
fant, oui, c'est elle! Ô mon Dieu, mon
child, yes, 'tis she! O my God, my
nis, je te bé - nis!
name! thy name I praise!
(violently agitated.)
Ah!
Ah!
nis, je te bé - nis!
name! thy name I praise!
(dismayed)
Mi - gnon!
Mi - gnon!
Dieu, je te bé - nis!
God, thy name I praise!
(supporting her)
Ma fil - le!
My daughter!
(as if suffocating)
Je meurs!
I die!
(she staggers)
(she falls)
Je
I
Dieu! qu'a-t-el-le donc!
Heav'ns! What has be-fall'n?
Grand Dieu!
Oh Heav'ns!
Ah! Spe-ra-ta!
Ah! Spe-ra-ta!

(Wilhelm goes to open the window)
Andantino con moto.
Lothario.
M.
L.
meurs!
die!
Non! ne meurs pas, chère en-fant!
No, do not die, darling child!
Wilhelm (returning to Mignon).
W.
Le bonheur est i - ci maintenant!
In this house shall be joy ev-er-more!
un poco riten.
(Mignon gradually comes to herself.)
W.
El-le re-vit!
She is re-viving!
Chè-re Mi - gnon! Je t'ai - me! oui, je
Dearest Mi - gnon! I love you! yes, I
Lothario.
L.
Son cœur se sou-vient!
Her sens-es re - turn!
Mignon (recognizing Lothario and Wilhelm).
(as if in a trance)
W.
M.
dim.
t'ai - me!
love you!
Ah! c'est là que je vou-lais
Ah! 'Tis there, in love ev-er

M.
vi - vre, Ai - mer, ai - mer et mou - rir! C'est
fond - er, I fain would live and die! 'Tis
W.
Wilhelm.
p
Son coeur se sou -
Her sens - es re -
M.
cresc.
là que je voulais vi - vre,
there! in love ev-er fond - er,
ff
C'est
'Tis
W.
f
ff
vient! Chè - re Mi-gnon! C'est
turn! Dear-est Mi-gnon! 'Tis
L.
Lothario.
ff
Ah!
Ah!
C'est
'Tis
cresc.
M.
là que je vou-lais vi - vre, Ai -
there, in love ev - er fond - er, I
W.
là que tu dois vi - vre Pour
there, in love ev - er fond - er, From
L.
là,
there,
là que tu dois vi -
in love ev-er fond -
ff
6
15470

M.
mer, ai - mer et mou - rir! C'est
fain would live and die! 'Tis
W.
être heu - reu - se et pour ai - mer! C'est
woe a - wak - ing, life shall be joy! 'Tis
L.
vre, pour être heu - reu - se, heu -
er, from woe a - wak - ing, a -
M.
là que je vou - lais vi - vre! C'est
there, in love ev - er fond - er, I'd
W.
là que tu dois vi - vre!
there, in love e'er fond - er,
L.
reu - se et pour ai -
wak - ing, life shall be
Allegro.
M.
là! oui, c'est là! Mon
live, I would die! Ah, my
W.
oui, c'est là! pour tou -
Ay, 'tis there! Life shall
L.
mer! oui, c'est là! Wil -
joy! Ay, 'tis there! Ah,
Allegro.
sf
sf

M.
père! mon pays! ô mon Dieu! je te bé-nis! je
own, my native land! O my God! I praise thy name! Thy
W.
jours u-nis! ô mon Dieu! je te bé-nis! je
be a joy! O my God! I praise thy name! Thy
L.
helm, sois mon fils! ô mon Dieu! mon Dieu! je
Wil-helm, my son! O my God! my God! Thy
ff
te bé-nis!
name I praise!
ff
End of the Opera.

Appendix
of
Interpolated Music.

1st Act of Mignon.

2nd verse of Lothario's song, as sung by M. Faure at London.

(See page 16.)

L.

moin. ———— El-le vit, el-le vit, et je cherche sa
bled. ———— She's a-live! she's a-live! E'er do I seek her

L.

dim. *p*

tra - - - ce! Je me re-pose un
trac - - - es: Here will I rest a

p

L.

p

jour, un seul jour, et je pas - se! je vais plus loin, toujours plus
day, for a day, swiftly pass - es; Then further on, still on I

(continue page 16, meas.1.)

L.

dim. *p*

loin, ———— toujours plus loin! ————
fare, ———— still on I fare! ————

a tempo

p

p

2nd Act of Mignon.

Air of Filina.

Sung by Mme Volpini at London.

(See page 166.)

F.
ne! Te voi - là vraiment dans ton é - lé - ment; dans ton é - lé -
na! In thy el - e - ment art thou for a while, art thou for a
p
ment! Tour - men - te, lu - ti - ne et trom - pe tour a
while! Tor - ment them, al - lure them, and tease them turn by
tour Tous ces mal - heu - reux af - fo - lés d'a -
turn, All these hap - less ones for thy love who
mf
mour! A - ler - te, a - ler - te, Phi
burn! A - rouse thee, a - rouse thee, Fi
li - ne! Tour - men - te et lu - ti - ne, Trom -
li - na! Tor - ment them, al - lure them, tease
sf

p
rit.
F.
-pe tour à tour Ces malheu-reux af-fo-lés d'a-mour! Tous ces mal-heu-
—them turn by turn, These hap-less ones for thy love who burn! These hap-less ones
pp
colla voce
reux af-fo-lés d'a-mour! Tour-mente et lu-ti-ne, Trom-pe tour à
for thy love — who burn. Tor-ment them, al-lure them, and tease turn by
p
string.
cresc.
tour Tous ces mal-heu-reux af-fo-lés d'a-mour, — d'a-
turn, These hap-less ones for thy love who burn, — who —
string.
f
molto ritenuto a piacere
mour! Tour-men-te, tour-men-te, tour-men-te, lu-
burn, Tor-ment them, al-lure them, tor-ment — them, al-
colla voce
string.
ti-ne Tous ces mal-heu-reux af-fo-lés — d'a-
lure — them, These hap-less ones for thy love — who
string.

a piacere

F.

mour! ah! d'amour!
burn! Ah! who burn!

f *f* *p* *f*

(sighing) *p a piacere*

F.

Ah! pour-tant!
Ah! but then!

a piacere *f*

Andante.

dol.

F.

J'a-vais fait un plus doux rê-ve! Un autre a-vait touché mon-
'Twas a fair-er dream: a lov-er Had found a way to melt my

p *pp*

F.

cœur! A-vant que la nuit s'a-chè-ve Le re-ver-rai-
heart; Ere night-fall 'twill be o-ver. Shall I see him once a-

poco accel. *cresc.* *dim.* *rit.*

F.

je? Le re-ver-rai-je? est-ce lui, est-ce lui qui
gain? but once a-gain? Is it he, is it he shall

poco accel. *riten.*

pp
dim.
sera mon vainqueur? Ah! j'avais fait un autre
defy all my art? Ah! 'twas a fairer dream: a
dolciss.
cresc.
rêve, Ce jeune homme avait su toucher mon cœur. Le reverraije avant que la fête s'achève? Est-ce lui qui sera mon vainqueur? ah! mon vainqueur?
lover Had found away to melt my heart! Ah, shall I see him ere the long festal is over? Is it he shall defy all my art? Ah! all my art?
Allegro. Tempo I.
f (gaily)
p
Bah! s'il m'ou-
Bah! Should he
fp

F.

blie, ou-bli-ons au-si, Et ri-ons aux dé-
not think on me, then I Can for-get him, as

Variant. *a piacere*
ah! Tour-
ah! Tor-

F. *cresc.* *f* *p*

pens de ceux qui sont i-ci! Ah! Tour-
well, and laugh while lov-ers sigh! Ah! Tor-

cresc. *f*

F.

men-te,_ lu-ti-ne Et trom-pe tour à tour
ment them, al-lure_ them, and tease_ them turn by turn,

p

F.

Tous ces_ mal-heu-reux af-fo-lés d'a-mour!
All these_ hap-less ones_ for_ thy love who burn!

F. *mf*

A-ler-te, a-ler-te, Phi-li-ne! Tour-
A-rouse thee, a-rouse thee, Fi-li-na! Tor-

F.
mente et lu - ti - ne,
ment them, al - lure them!
Tour-mente et lu-
Tor-ment them, al-
ti - ne, trom-pe tour à tour
lure them, tease them turn by turn,
Tous ces mal-heu-reux af-
All these hap-less ones for
fo - lés d'a - mour!
thy love who burn!
Trom-pe tour à tour
Tease them turn by turn,
tous ces mal-heu-reux af-
All these hap-less ones for
Var.
fo - lés d'a - mour!
thy love who burn!
fo - lés d'a - mour! ah!
thy love who burn! Ah!
cresc.

Continue with the Allegretto in $\frac{6}{8}$ time on page 167.

2nd Act of Mignon.

Rondo-Gavotte.

Sung by Mme Trebelli-Bettini at London.

(See page 201.)

F. cœur, je sens mon cœur bat - tre d'es - poir. Ah! je
heart, I feel my heart beat high with hope! Ah, I

F. guet - te l'ins - tant de la_ re - voir.___
wait__ for the hour when we__ shall meet.___

F. Oui, je sens mon cœur, je sens mon cœur bat - tre d'es -
Yes, I feel my heart, I feel my heart beat high with

F. poir! Co - quet - te, je guet - te l'ins - tant de_ te re -
hope! Co - quette, here I wait_ for the hour when we shall

F. voir! Il_ faut en - fin vain - cre la cru -
meet! Ah, cru - el fair, in the end I'll

F.
p
3
el - le,
vanquish,
Il _ faut tou - cher, toucher le cœur de _ l'in - fi -
She _ must be made, she must be made to _ heed my
f
p
p
cresc.
p
dè - le, Il _ faut tou - cher le _ cœur de l'in - fi - dè - - le! Je
an - guish! She must be made to _ heed, to heed my an - - guish! I'm
cresc.
dim.
p
suis dans son bou - doir Et je sens mon cœur, je sens mon cœur bat - tre d'es -
here in her bou - doir, And I feel my heart, I feel my heart beat high with
poir! Ah! je guet - te l'ins - tant de _ la re -
hope! Ah, I wait _ for the hour when we shall
cresc.
tr
voir. Moi, _ je _ veux qu'on
meet. I _ would have her
f
f
p

F.
m'ai-me et j'es pè - - re, oui, j'es-père à mon tour être heu-
love me, and I hope, ah, yes, I hope to en-joy, as I
F.
reux; Tant pis, ma foi! pour tous ses a-mou-reux, tant pis pour tous ses a-mou-
woo! How sad 'twill be for all who love her too! How sad for all who love her
cresc.
dim.
F.
reux! tant pis, ma foi! Je suis dans son bou-doir Et je sens mon
too, who love her too! I'm here in her bou-doir, and I feel my
p
F.
cœur, je sens mon cœur bat-tre d'es-poir. Ah! je guet-te l'ins-
heart, I feel my heart beat high with hope! Oh, I wait for the
tr
F.
tant de la-re-voir, Ah! je sens mon
hour when we shall meet. Ah! I feel my
p

Continue p. 202, line 2, second measure of Recitative.